A VECTOR APPROACH TO OSCILLATIONS

ACADEMIC PAPERBACKS*

EDITED BY Henry Booker, D. Allan Bromley, Nicholas DeClaris, W. Magnus, Alvin Nason, and A. Shenitzer

---

BIOLOGY

Design and Function at the Threshold of Life: The Viruses HEINZ FRAENKEL-CONRAT
The Evolution of Genetics ARNOLD W. RAVIN
Isotopes in Biology GEORGE WOLF
Life: Its Nature, Origin, and Development A. I. OPARIN
Time, Cells, and Aging BERNARD L. STREHLER

ENGINEERING

A Vector Approach to Oscillations HENRY BOOKER
Dynamic Programming and Modern Control Theory RICHARD BELLMAN and ROBERT KALABA

MATHEMATICS

Finite Permutation Groups HELMUT WIELANDT
Elements of Abstract Harmonic Analysis GEORGE BACHMAN
The Method of Averaging Functional Corrections: Theory and Applications A. YU. LUCHKA
Geometric Transformations (in two volumes) P. S. MODENOV and A. S. PARKHOMENKO
Representation Theory of Finite Groups MARTIN BURROW
Introduction to *p*-Adic Numbers and Valuation Theory GEORGE BACHMAN
Linear Operators in Hilbert Space WERNER SCHMEIDLER
Noneuclidean Geometry HERBERT MESCHKOWSKI
Quadratic Forms and Matrices N. V. YEFIMOV

PHYSICS

Crystals: Their Role in Nature and in Science CHARLES BUNN
Elementary Dynamics of Particles H. W. HARKNESS
Elementary Plane Rigid Dynamics H. W. HARKNESS
Mössbauer Effect: Principles and Applications GUNTHER K. WERTHEIM
Potential Barriers in Semiconductors B. R. GOSSICK
Principles of Vector Analysis JERRY B. MARION

*Most of these volumes are also available in a cloth bound edition.

A VECTOR APPROACH TO OSCILLATIONS

HENRY G. BOOKER

PROFESSOR OF APPLIED ELECTROPHYSICS
UNIVERSITY OF CALIFORNIA AT SAN DIEGO
LA JOLLA, CALIFORNIA

ACADEMIC PRESS New York and London

ACADEMIC PRESS INC.
111 Fifth Avenue, New York, New York 10003

United Kingdom Edition published by
ACADEMIC PRESS INC. (LONDON) LTD.
Berkeley Square House, London W.1

LIBRARY OF CONGRESS CATALOG CARD NUMBER: 65-19801

PRINTED IN THE UNITED STATES OF AMERICA

PREFACE

There are many ways in which oscillations arise in physics and engineering. This book presents an approach to the processes of thought involved in handling oscillations. For most purposes, sinusoidal oscillations are best illustrated graphically not by sinuous curves but by projection of rotating vectors. Indeed this is what is involved in the use of a right angled triangle in trigonometry to introduce the sine and cosine functions. Thus the process of graphical representation of oscillations involves the drawing and interpretation of vector diagrams. The mathematical analysis illustrated by these diagrams is therefore a vector analysis. Superposition of oscillations involves vector addition, and when a continuous spectrum of oscillations is to be handled, the vector addition becomes vector integration. Mathematical representation of oscillations by means of rotating vectors consequently begins in the domain of vector algebra and develops into the domain of vector calculus. It is an objective of this book to ascertain and develop the vector algebra required to represent oscillations.

The necessary vector algebra and calculus already exist in textbooks on mathematics under such titles as "Complex Numbers," "Functions of a Complex Variable," and "Contour Integration in the Complex Plane." Unfortunately these books are written in a language alien to the process of thinking about oscillations in terms of rotating vectors. If we adopt the language of pure mathematics, we become involved in describing rotating vectors in a language that is peculiar to the point of being deceiving. In this language a uniformly rotating vector of unit magnitude is described by means of the "exponential function of an imaginary number proportional to time." Now the very object of introducing rotating vectors to describe oscillations is to provide a vivid picture of what is involved. The powerful vehicle of thought thus acquired is sabotaged if we now describe a rotating vector in such fanciful language as an "exponential function of an imaginary number proportional to time." Analysis in terms of rotating vectors, together with the associated vector algebra and calculus, is the technique required to handle oscillations, but we need a more commonsense language in which to convey our meaning than the language of "imaginary numbers." It is an objective of this book to devise and employ a straightforward language for describing rotating vectors.

In devising a commonsense language for the vector algebra required to study oscillations, some novel terms are introduced. If $\mathbf{s}$ is a fixed vector and t denotes time, it is necessary to understand why $e^{\mathbf{s}t}$ represents a spiraling vector. The expression "complex frequency" for $\mathbf{s}$ does not meet the requirements of a commonsense language. The component in the reference direction of the spiraling vector $e^{\mathbf{s}t}$ varies with time. The type of activity involved in this time variation is determined by the magnitude and direction of the vector $\mathbf{s}$. This activity can range from an exponential rise or decay to a sinusoidal oscillation. Since the vector $\mathbf{s}$ describes the character of the activity involved, it has been called the "actance." What is often called the "complex frequency plane" then becomes an "actance diagram."

In using vector algebra to represent oscillations, little use is found for the "scalar product" of two vectors or for the "vector product" of two vectors. On the other hand, given two vectors, a great deal of use is found for a coplanar vector whose magnitude is the product of the magnitudes of the two given vectors and whose counterclockwise angle with the reference direction is the sum of the angles for the two given vectors. This type of product is referred to in this book as the "planar product" of the vectors. Apart from the expressions "planar product" and "actance," the language employed in the book may reasonably be described as vernacular. Except for relating the language here used to the language of pure mathematics, use of such expressions as "complex number," "real part," "imaginary part," and so on, is avoided, while at the same time specific use is made of the ideas that mathematicians refer to as "functions of a complex variable." In other words a conscientious effort has been made always to call a spade a spade.

The vectors employed in the book are sometimes known as "phase vectors"; this is to distinguish them from "field vectors," such as the electric vector, the magnetic vector, the gravitational vector, and so on. Contracted expressions such as "phasor" and "fieldor" may also be used if desired. Use of the expressions phase vector and field vector invites the question: What is the conceptual difference between a phase vector and a field vector? The answer is: None. A vector is a quantity that has magnitude and direction and that resolves according to the cosine law. Both phase vectors and field vectors have magnitude and direction and resolve according to cosine law. Both phase vectors and field vectors are therefore simply vectors. Of course, it is true that when using phase vectors one is mainly interested in the planar product, whereas when using field vectors one is mainly interested in the scalar and vector products. It is also true that the planar product depends on the orientation of the reference direction, whereas the scalar and vector products are independent of the orientation of the frame of reference. However, these are distinctions between types of product, not types of vector. It has therefore been thought wise to call the vectors involved in this book simply vectors, although there is no objection to calling them phase vectors, phasors, or complex numbers if desired.

Although the book presents in commonsense language a number of ideas about complex numbers, the book is not intended to replace a mathematical treatment. Study of the mathematical theory of functions of a complex variable is specifically recommended. What the book does is to present those elementary ideas about complex numbers that are most frequently not understood or misunderstood by students of physics and engineering. The accent is on the creation of vivid concepts, not on adherence to tradition. Although the book cannot be described as a conventional textbook, problems are nevertheless included.

The book was prepared while the author was IBM Professor of Engineering and Applied Mathematics at Cornell University.

HENRY G. BOOKER

La Jolla, California
July, 1965

CONTENTS

CHAPTER 4

The Exponential Function of a Vector

Problems

CHAPTER 1

THE TECHNIQUE OF HANDLING OSCILLATIONS

1.1. Introduction

A large number of situations encountered in physics and engineering involve oscillations, and a tremendous amount of science is intimately bound up with the technique of handling oscillations. The simplest example of an oscillation is a sinusoidal oscillation represented by an expression of the form

$$a(t) = A \cos(\omega t + \alpha) \tag{1.1}$$

where t denotes time and the quantities A, ω, and α are parameters that are independent of time. If the time-function given by Eq. (1.1) is plotted as a function of t, we obtain the graph shown in Fig. 1.1. The periodic time is $2\pi/\omega$, and the frequency of oscillation is $\omega/(2\pi)$ cycles per unit time. The function oscillates between the extreme positive value A and the extreme negative value $-A$; the quantity A is known as the amplitude of the oscillation. Prior to time zero, the function last achieves its maximum value A at the time $-\alpha/\omega$. The parameter α is thus a measure of this time, and is known as the phase of the oscillation. Sinusoidal functions of time may always be represented graphically as shown in Fig. 1.1, but for most purposes this graphical representation is not the most convenient one to use.

The lack of convenience associated with representing a sinusoidal function graphically in the manner illustrated in Fig. 1.1 may be demonstrated with the aid of Fig. 1.2.

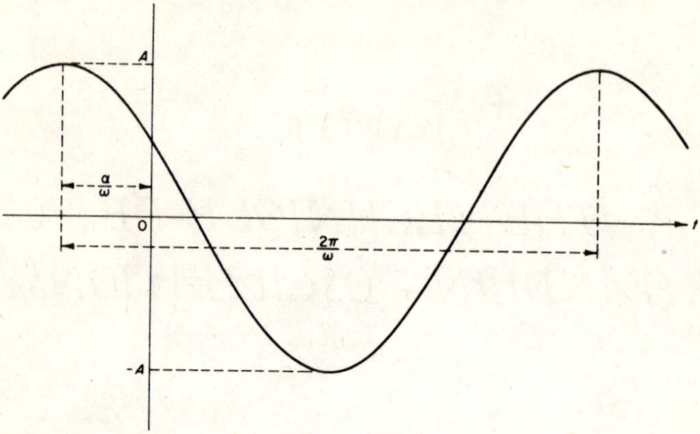

FIG. 1.1. Illustrating a sinusoidal oscillation of angular frequency ω, amplitude A, and phase α.

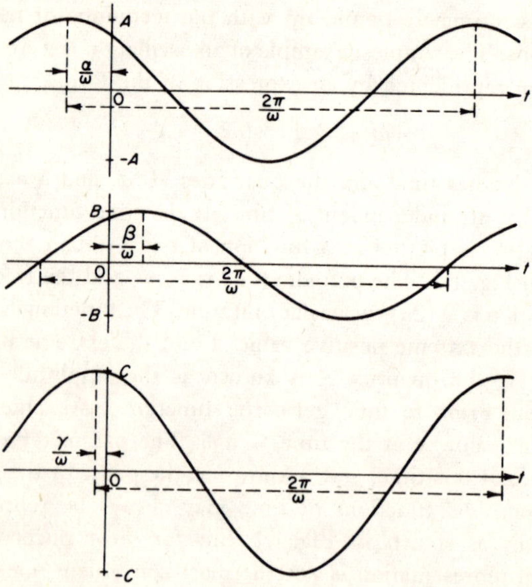

FIG. 1.2. Illustrating the addition of two sinusoidal oscillations of the same frequency, but of different amplitudes and phases, to give a resultant sinusoidal oscillation.

Figure 1.2(a) is a graphical representation of the oscillation

$$a(t) = A \cos(\omega t + \alpha) \tag{1.2}$$

while Fig. 1.2(b) is a graphical representation of the oscillation

$$b(t) = B \cos(\omega t + \beta). \tag{1.3}$$

The two oscillations given by Eqs. (1.2) and (1.3) have the same frequency, but have different amplitudes and phases. Let us now suppose that we have to form the sum of these two oscillations and to plot as a function of time the expression

$$c(t) = A \cos(\omega t + \alpha) + B \cos(\omega t + \beta). \tag{1.4}$$

To do this we can measure the ordinates in Fig. 1.2(a) and Fig. 1.2(b) for a series of values of t, and then add these ordinates with due regard to sign. By carrying out this tedious process we then arrive at the graph shown in Fig. 1.2(c), which therefore represents Eq. (1.4). From Fig. 1.2(c) we notice that the function given by expression (1.4) is in fact another sinusoidal oscillation of the same frequency and may therefore be written in the form

$$c(t) = C \cos(\omega t + \gamma). \tag{1.5}$$

Moreover, from the graph shown in Fig. 1.2(c) we may read off values for the amplitude C and the phase γ of the oscillation represented by Eq. (1.4). Alternatively, instead of making this calculation graphically, it is possible to carry it out analytically. By means of well-known trigonometrical formulas, it is possible to write Eq. (1.4) in the form of Eq. (1.5) and so to derive analytical expressions for C and γ in terms of A, α, B, and β. Even without writing down the appropriate formulas, it is clear that the analytical process of summing the two oscillations given by Eqs. (1.2) and (1.3), and deriving the amplitude and phase of the resultant oscillation, is quite as tedious as the process of ordinate addition illustrated in Fig. 1.2.

The process of adding two sinusoidal oscillations of the same frequency, but of different amplitudes and phases, is one of the simplest operations that has to be carried out in discussing oscillatory phenomena. It is clear, therefore, that some far more powerful method for handling sinusoidal oscillations must be found than that represented graphically in Fig. 1.2 and analytically in Eqs. (1.2) through (1.5).

The graphical method for representing a sinusoidal oscillation required to supplant that shown in Fig. 1.1 involves the use of a rotating vector in the manner illustrated in Fig. 1.3. In Fig. 1.3

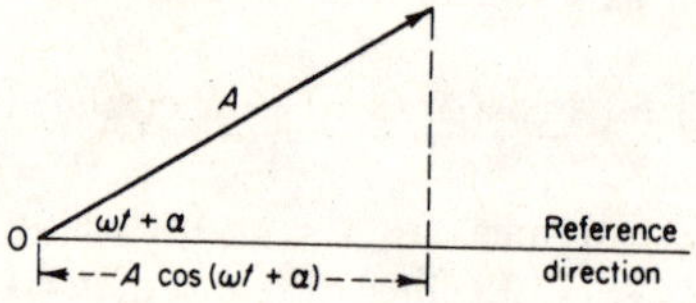

FIG. 1.3. Illustrating the use of a rotating vector to represent a sinusoidal oscillation.

a vector of magnitude A is drawn at angle $\omega t + \alpha$ to a reference direction, which is taken horizontally to the right. With lapse of time t, the vector rotates in the counterclockwise direction with angular velocity ω. The component of the vector in the reference direction is given by Eq. (1.1). It follows therefore that, to represent the oscillation given by Eq. (1.1) graphically, we may use a vector of length A rotating with angular velocity ω. The phase α of the oscillation specifies the angle that the vector makes with the reference direction at time zero. We shall find that the representation of an oscillation as the component along a reference direction of a rotating vector as illustrated in Fig. 1.3 is enormously more convenient than the graphical representation shown in Fig. 1.1. The almost universal representation of oscillations by means of rotating vectors is illustrated by the fact that the angular velocity ω of the rotating vector is called the angular frequency of the oscillation and is measured in radians per unit time.

1.2. The Addition and Subtraction of Oscillations Using Vectors

Let us suppose that we have two oscillations of the same frequency but of different amplitudes and phases, represented by Eqs. (1.2) and (1.3). Let us suppose that we wish to form the sum of these two oscillations in accordance with Eq. (1.4). Let us represent the oscillation in Eq. (1.2) as the component along the reference direction of a vector of magnitude A making at time t an angle $\omega t + \alpha$ with the reference direction. In the same way, let us represent the oscillation in Eq. (1.3) by a vector of length B making at time t an angle $\omega t + \beta$ with the reference direction. These vectors are denoted by

$$\mathbf{A} = A \angle \omega t + \alpha \tag{1.6}$$

and

$$\mathbf{B} = B \angle \omega t + \beta. \tag{1.7}$$

Their positions at time t are illustrated in Fig. 1.4. Now consider

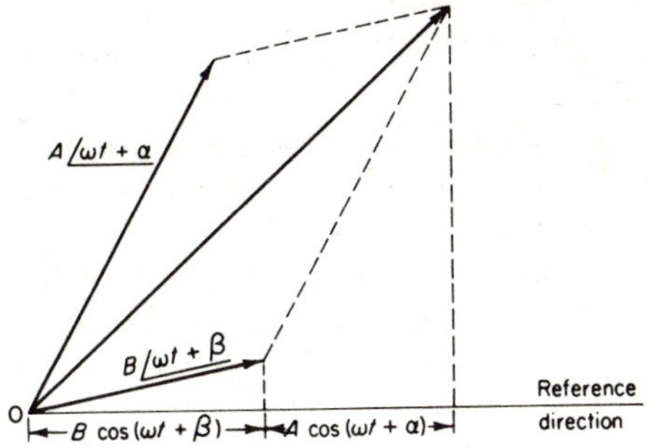

FIG. 1.4. Illustrating the use of vector addition for summing two oscillations.

the vector formed by taking the vector sum of the two vectors given by Eqs. (1.6) and (1.7). This vector is shown in Fig. 1.4 as the diagonal of a parallelogram. From the geometry of Fig. 1.4, it is clear that the component of this resultant vector along the reference direction is the sum of the components along the reference direction of the vectors **A** and **B**. It follows that the component along the reference direction of the resultant vector in Fig. 1.4 is equal to the expression on the right-hand side of Eq. (1.4), and this is the sum of the given oscillations. The sum of the two oscillations in Eqs. (1.2) and (1.3) is therefore the component along the reference direction of the vector sum of the two vectors in Eqs. (1.6) and (1.7).

Since the vectors **A** and **B** are rotating with the same angular velocity ω, the resultant of the two vectors is rotating with the same angular velocity ω. The parallelogram in Fig. 1.4 is therefore rotating with angular velocity ω without changing its shape.

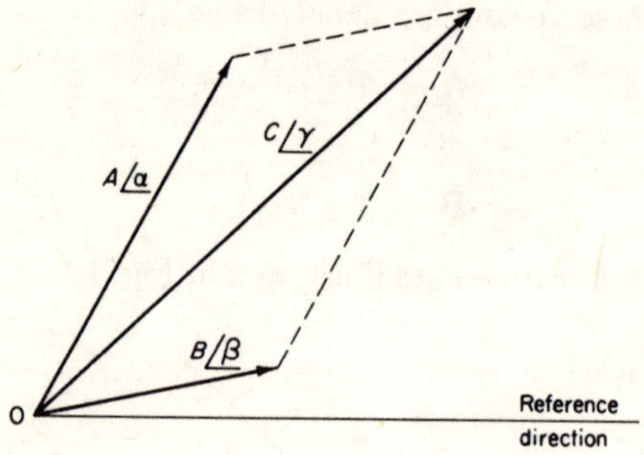

FIG. 1.5. Showing the positions at time zero of the rotating vectors illustrated in Fig. 1.4.

Let the positions of the vectors at time zero be as shown in Fig. 1.5. At this time the vectors **A** and **B** are

$$A \angle\alpha \tag{1.8}$$

and

$$B \angle\beta. \tag{1.9}$$

Let the resultant vector at time zero be

$$C \angle\gamma. \tag{1.10}$$

Then it follows that, at time t, the resultant of the vectors given by Eqs. (1.6) and (1.7) is

$$\mathbf{C} = C \angle\omega t + \gamma. \tag{1.11}$$

The component of this vector along the reference direction at time t is

$$C \cos(\omega t + \gamma) \tag{1.12}$$

and this is the sum of the two oscillations given in Eqs. (1.2) and (1.3).

We thus see that, to find the amplitude and phase of the sum of two oscillations of the same frequency, we proceed as follows. We represent the two oscillations by means of rotating vectors and draw the positions of the vectors at time zero as shown in Fig. 1.5. We form the vector sum of the two vectors at this time and let the resulting vector have magnitude C and angle γ. Then the two given oscillations of angular frequency ω combine to give an oscillation of the same angular frequency ω with amplitude C and phase γ.

This method of forming the sum of two oscillations of the same frequency but of different amplitudes and phases is greatly superior to that illustrated in Fig. 1.2. Moreover, the vector method of adding two oscillations is not restricted to a situation in which they are both of the same frequency. If the given oscillations are of different frequency, the two vectors to be added in Fig. 1.4 are rotating with different angular velocities. The end of the resultant vector does not then describe a circle, but its component along the reference direction still represents the sum of the two oscillations. It is clear therefore that, in all circumstances, great advantage accrues from representing an oscillation as the component of a rotating vector along a reference direction.

It frequently happens that all the oscillations with which we are concerned have the same angular frequency ω. In these circumstances all the vectors representing these oscillations are rotating with the same angular velocity ω, and the same is true of any vector combination of these vectors that may be required in adding the oscillations. We thus have a situation in which the lengths of all vectors with which we are concerned stay constant and their relative angular positions remain unchanged. The whole vector diagram rotates solidly with angular velocity ω. Under these circumstances all vectors may be conveniently drawn for a selected time, such as time zero. This procedure is illustrated in Figs. 1.4 and 1.5. From the vector diagram shown in Fig. 1.5 for time zero, the vector diagram for any other time t is obtained by rotating the vector diagram solidly through an angle ωt in the counterclockwise direction, as shown in Fig. 1.4. Any information about any of the oscillations at any time t may be derived in this way from the vector diagram for time zero. In situations where all the oscillations with which we are concerned have the same angular frequency ω, the practice is to represent the oscillations by means of rotating vectors and to draw a vector diagram appropriate to time zero. The magnitudes of the vectors are then the amplitudes of the oscillations, and the angles that the vectors make with the reference direction are the phases of the oscillations.

1.3. Use of the Quotient of Two Vectors to Represent the Amplitude Ratio and Phase Difference of Two Oscillations

Let us suppose that we have two oscillations of the same frequency, the first being of amplitude A and phase α, and the second being of amplitude B and phase β. Let the two oscillations be represented as the components along a reference direction of a pair of rotating vectors. At time zero, let the vectors be

$$\mathbf{A} = A \angle \alpha \tag{1.13}$$

and

$$\mathbf{B} = B \angle \beta \tag{1.14}$$

and let the two vectors be as shown in Fig. 1.6. It frequently happens in practice that, given a pair of oscillations of the same frequency, it is necessary to make a comparison between them. This involves studying their amplitude ratio and their phase difference. If the two oscillations are represented by rotating vectors, and these vectors at time zero are given by Eqs. (1.13) and (1.14), the amplitude ratio for the oscillations is

$$\frac{A}{B} \tag{1.15}$$

while the phase difference between them is

$$\alpha - \beta. \tag{1.16}$$

Expression (1.15) is the ratio of the amplitude of the first oscillation to that of the second, while expression (1.16) is the angle by which the phase of the first oscillation leads the phase of the second.

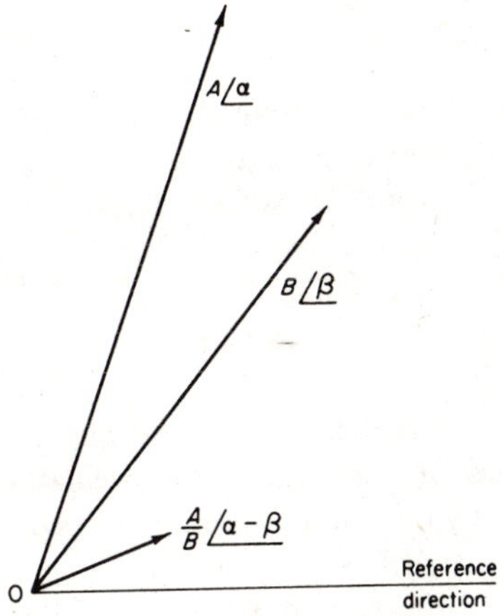

FIG. 1.6. Illustrating the use of the quotient of two vectors to represent the amplitude ratio and phase difference of a pair of oscillations of the same frequency.

A convenient way of studying the amplitude ratio and the phase difference of a pair of oscillations of the same frequency is to form a vector for which expression (1.15) is the magnitude and expression (1.16) is the angle with the reference direction. This vector is denoted by

$$\frac{A}{B} \angle \alpha - \beta \tag{1.17}$$

and may be represented as shown in Fig. 1.6. The length of the vector given by expression (1.17) is the ratio of the lengths of the other two vectors in Fig. 1.6; the angle that the vector given by expression (1.17) makes with the reference direction is equal to the angle between the other two vectors in Fig. 1.6. The process of forming the vector given by expression (1.17) from the vector given by Eqs. (1.13) and (1.14) is one of the commonest processes involved in handling oscillations. It is convenient to call the vector given by expression (1.17) the quotient of the vectors given by Eqs. (1.13) and (1.14) and to write

$$\frac{\mathbf{A}}{\mathbf{B}} = \frac{A}{B} \angle \alpha - \beta. \tag{1.18}$$

Thus the quotient of the vector **A**, whose magnitude is A and which makes a counterclockwise angle α with the reference direction, by the vector **B**, whose magnitude is B and which makes a counterclockwise angle β with the reference direction, is a vector whose magnitude is A/B and which makes with the reference direction the counterclockwise angle $\alpha - \beta$, as shown in Fig. 1.6.

It follows from the definition of the quotient of two vectors that the process of comparing two oscillations of the same frequency given by the reference components of a pair of rotating vectors may be carried out by forming the quotient of the two rotating vectors. Suppose that one of the oscillations has angular frequency ω, amplitude A, and phase α, so that it is the reference component of the rotating vector

$$A \angle \omega t + \alpha. \tag{1.19}$$

Suppose that the second oscillation has the same frequency ω but a different amplitude B and a different phase β. Let it be the reference component of the rotating vector

$$B \angle \omega t + \beta. \tag{1.20}$$

Now form the quotient of the vector given by expression (1.19) by the vector given by expression (1.20) in accordance with the definition given in Eq. (1.18). In the process of subtracting the angles, the quantity ωt cancels out, and the quotient vector is

$$\frac{A}{B} \angle \alpha - \beta. \tag{1.21}$$

Thus the quotient of the rotating vectors representing the two oscillations is a vector whose magnitude is the amplitude ratio of the two oscillations and whose angle is the phase difference between the two oscillations. Great importance thus attaches not only to the representation of oscillations as the reference components of rotating vectors but also to the calculation of the quotients of the rotating vectors, in accordance with the definition given in Eq. (1.18), in order to compare the amplitudes and phases of the oscillations.

1.4. The Planar Product of Two Vectors

In statics and dynamics, as well as in electricity and magnetism, use is frequently made of the scalar product of two vectors and of the vector product of two vectors. In using vectors to represent oscillations, however, comparatively little use exists for the scalar product and vector product of two vectors. On the other hand, considerable use exists for a type of product of two vectors that undoes the quotient operation described in the previous section. Thus suppose that, in accordance with Eq. (1.18), we have taken the quotient of a vector **A** by a vector **B** and obtained the vector

$$\mathbf{C} = \frac{\mathbf{A}}{\mathbf{B}}. \tag{1.22}$$

Then it is desirable to be able to combine the vectors **B** and **C** so as to recover the vector **A**. This type of product of two vectors undoes the quotient operation described in the previous section and is repeatedly required in using vectors to handle oscillations. It will be convenient to call this type of product of two vectors the "planar product"; all the vectors concerned in a planar product lie in a plane.

The planar product of the vectors

$$\mathbf{A} = A \angle \alpha \tag{1.23}$$

and

$$\mathbf{B} = B \angle \beta \tag{1.24}$$

is defined as the vector whose magnitude is AB and which makes with the reference direction an angle $\alpha + \beta$, measured in the counterclockwise direction. This statement is written

$$\mathbf{AB} = AB \angle\alpha + \beta \tag{1.25}$$

and is illustrated in Fig. 1.7. To formulate the planar product in

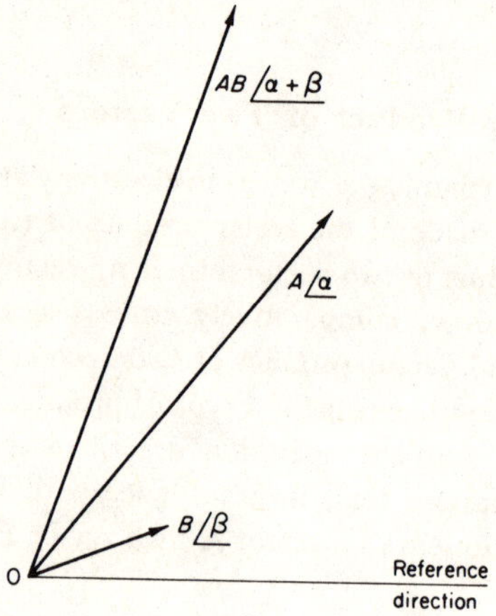

FIG. 1.7. Illustrating the planar product of two vectors.

Fig. 1.7 of the vectors specified by Eqs. (1.23) and (1.24), we multiply the magnitudes of the vectors and add their angles, thereby arriving at the vector given by Eq. (1.25). It does not matter whether we take the planar product of the vector **A** by the vector **B**, or the planar product of the vector **B** by the vector **A**. In either case we arrive at the vector given by Eq. (1.25) and illustrated in Fig. 1.7. Moreover, if we take the quotient of the vector in Eq. (1.25) by the vector in Eq. (1.24) in accordance with the definition in the previous section, we recover the vector in Eq. (1.23). Likewise, if we form the quotient of the vector in Eq. (1.25) by the vector in Eq. (1.23), we arrive at the vector in Eq. (1.24). The planar product of two vectors defined by

Eq. (1.25) is thus the reverse of the operation of forming the quotient defined by Eq. (1.18).

It is particularly to be noticed that, in forming the planar product of two vectors, the operation to be performed on the angles is one of addition. Likewise, in forming the quotient of two vectors, the operation to be performed on the angles is one of subtraction. The nomenclature "product" and "quotient" is associated with the operations performed on the magnitudes of the vectors.

It is also to be noticed that the vectors used to represent oscillations do not differ conceptually from the vectors used to represent electric and magnetic fields, or from the vectors used to represent force and velocity in mechanics. The vectors used in oscillation theory have the usual properties of vectors; they have magnitude and direction and resolve according to the cosine law. What is different in oscillation theory is the type of product of two vectors that is commonly encountered. Instead of scalar and vector products we shall encounter the planar product defined by Eq. (1.25), and in association with the planar product we shall encounter the quotient of two vectors defined by Eq. (1.18).

The results of this section and of the preceding section may be summarized in the following way. Let **A**, **B**, and **C** be three vectors. Let their magnitudes be denoted by $|\mathbf{A}|$, $|\mathbf{B}|$, $|\mathbf{C}|$, respectively. Let their counterclockwise angles with the reference direction be denoted by $\angle\mathbf{A}$, $\angle\mathbf{B}$, and $\angle\mathbf{C}$, respectively. If

$$\mathbf{C} = \mathbf{AB} \tag{1.26}$$

then

$$|\mathbf{C}| = |\mathbf{A}|\,|\mathbf{B}| \tag{1.27}$$

and

$$\angle\mathbf{C} = \angle\mathbf{A} + \angle\mathbf{B}. \tag{1.28}$$

If

$$\mathbf{C} = \mathbf{A}/\mathbf{B} \tag{1.29}$$

then

$$|\mathbf{C}| = |\mathbf{A}|/|\mathbf{B}| \tag{1.30}$$

and

$$\angle\mathbf{C} = \angle\mathbf{A} - \angle\mathbf{B}. \tag{1.31}$$

1.5. The Square Root of a Vector

In scalar algebra a positive number A has a square root B defined in such a way that the product of B with itself reproduces the number A. The number B is denoted by $A^{1/2}$ or $\sqrt{A}$, and it has two values that are equal in magnitude and opposite in sign. In vector algebra a vector **A** has a square-root vector **B** defined in such a way that the planar product of **B** with itself reproduces the vector **A**. The square-root vector **B** is denoted by $\mathbf{A}^{1/2}$ or $\sqrt{\mathbf{A}}$. By definition of the square-root vector **B** of the given vector **A**, it follows that

$$\mathbf{B}\mathbf{B} = \mathbf{A} \tag{1.32}$$

where the product on the left-hand side is a planar product. Equation (1.32) is conveniently written

$$\mathbf{B}^2 = \mathbf{A}. \tag{1.33}$$

Let

$$\mathbf{A} = A \angle\alpha \tag{1.34}$$

and

$$\mathbf{B} = B \angle\beta. \tag{1.35}$$

From the definition of the planar product, it follows that

$$\mathbf{B}^2 = B^2 \angle 2\beta. \tag{1.36}$$

In accordance with Eqs. (1.34) and (1.36), Eq. (1.33) states that

$$B^2 = A \tag{1.37}$$

and

$$2\beta = \alpha. \tag{1.38}$$

Equations (1.37) and (1.38) may be rewritten

$$B = A^{1/2} \tag{1.39}$$

and

$$\beta = \tfrac{1}{2}\alpha. \tag{1.40}$$

Equations (1.39) and (1.40) state that the square root of a vector **A** is a vector of length $|\mathbf{A}|^{1/2}$ making a counterclockwise angle $\frac{1}{2}\angle\mathbf{A}$ with the reference direction. The relation between the vectors $\mathbf{A}$ and $\mathbf{A}^{1/2}$ is therefore as shown in Fig. 1.8. The vector $\mathbf{A}^{1/2}$ has the property that the planar product of $\mathbf{A}^{1/2}$ with itself reproduces the vector $\mathbf{A}$.

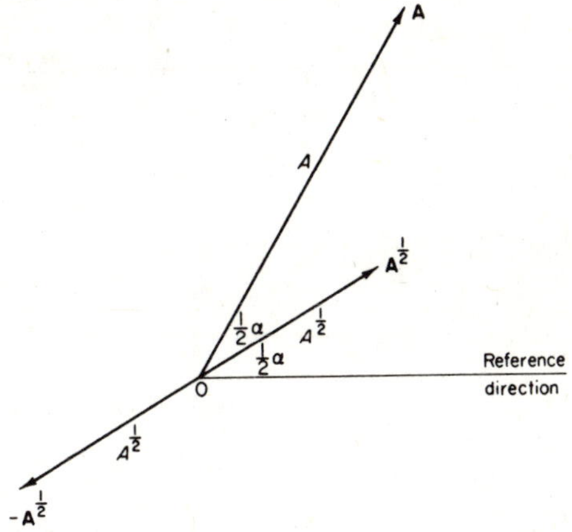

FIG. 1.8. Illustrating calculation of the square root of a vector **A**.

In Fig. 1.8 the vector $-\mathbf{A}^{1/2}$ also has the property that the planar product of $-\mathbf{A}^{1/2}$ with itself reproduces the vector $\mathbf{A}$. The magnitude of the vector $-\mathbf{A}^{1/2}$ is $A^{1/2}$, and the product of this magnitude with itself is the magnitude A of the vector $\mathbf{A}$; the counterclockwise angle of the vector $-\mathbf{A}^{1/2}$ in Fig. 1.8 is $-(\pi - \frac{1}{2}\alpha)$, and the addition of this angle with itself is $-(2\pi - \alpha)$, which gives the same direction as the counterclockwise angle α. Thus the vector $\mathbf{A}$ in Fig. 1.8 has two square-root vectors $\mathbf{A}^{1/2}$ and $-\mathbf{A}^{1/2}$ that are equal in magnitude and opposite in direction. It is usual, but not essential, to regard as the principal square-root of $\mathbf{A}$ that square-root vector whose direction is closer to the reference direction.

Two important special cases of the process of finding the square-root of a vector are illustrated in Fig. 1.9. In Fig. 1.9(a) the vector $\mathbf{A}$ points in the reference direction. The magnitude of the vector $\mathbf{A}^{1/2}$ is $A^{1/2}$, in accordance with Eq. (1.39). The angle of the vector $\mathbf{A}$ in Fig. 1.9(a) is 0 (or $\pm 2\pi$), and it therefore follows from Eq. (1.40) that the angle of the vector $\mathbf{A}^{1/2}$ is 0 or $\pm\pi$ as shown in Fig. 1.9(a). On the other hand, in Fig. 1.9(b) the vector **A** is in the direction opposite to the reference direction.

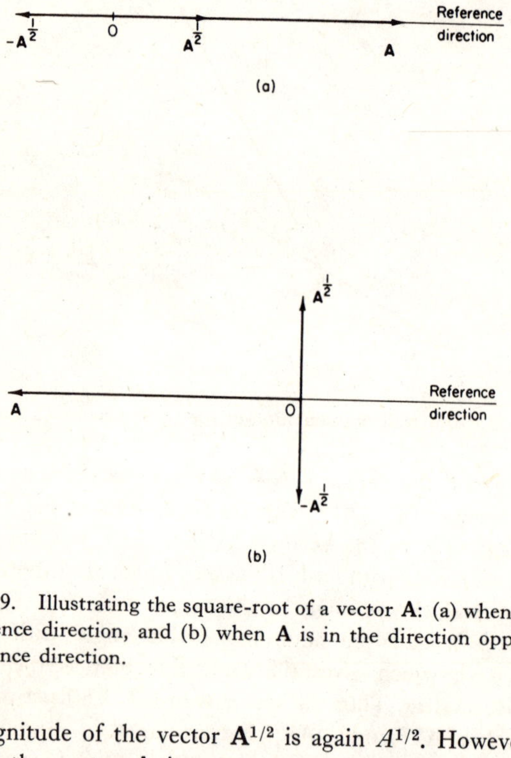

FIG. 1.9. Illustrating the square-root of a vector **A**: (a) when **A** is in the reference direction, and (b) when **A** is in the direction opposite to the reference direction.

The magnitude of the vector $\mathbf{A}^{1/2}$ is again $A^{1/2}$. However, the angle of the vector **A** is now $\pm\pi$, and it therefore follows from Eq. (1.40) that the angle of the vector $\mathbf{A}^{1/2}$ is $\pm\frac{1}{2}\pi$, as shown in Fig. 1.9(b). In this case it is usual, but not essential, to regard as the principal square root of **A** the square-root vector whose counterclockwise angle with the reference direction is $+\frac{1}{2}\pi$.

1.6. The Planar Product of Two Vectors in Cartesian Components

So far we have described a vector by means of its magnitude and direction, but it is also possible to represent a vector by means of its Cartesian components. It is usual for this purpose to take the x axis in the reference direction and the y axis perpendicular to this direction, as shown in Fig. 1.10. The positive

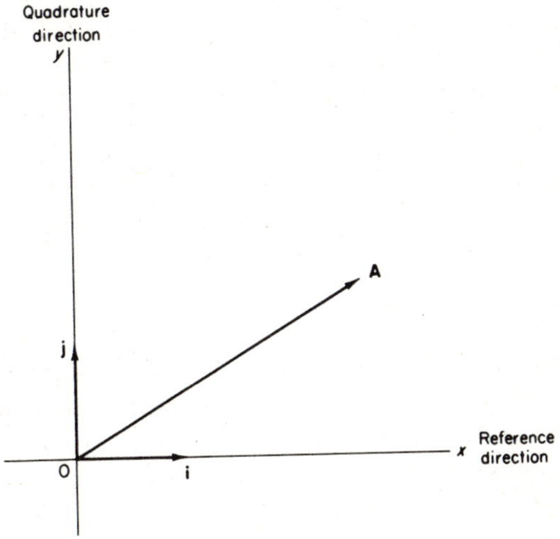

FIG. 1.10. Illustrating the use of the reference and quadrature directions as axes of Cartesian coordinates.

direction of the y axis is obtained from the positive direction of the x axis by rotation through a right-angle in the counter-clockwise direction. The positive direction of the y axis will be referred to as the quadrature direction, and the x and y components of a vector will be called the reference and quadrature components of the vector. In this terminology it is the reference component of a rotating vector that executes the oscillation represented by the vector.

Let $\mathbf{i}$ be a unit vector in the reference direction and $\mathbf{j}$ a unit vector in the quadrature direction, as indicated in Fig. 1.10.

Since **i** is a vector of unit magnitude at angle zero to the reference direction, while **j** is a vector of unit magnitude at a counter-clockwise angle $\frac{1}{2}\pi$ to the reference direction, we may write

$$\mathbf{i} = 1 \angle 0 \tag{1.41}$$

and

$$\mathbf{j} = 1 \angle \tfrac{1}{2}\pi. \tag{1.42}$$

Between these two vectors there exist some simple but important relations. Let us first consider a pair of unit vectors both pointing along the reference direction, and let us form their planar product in accordance with Eq. (1.25). From Eq. (1.41), the product of the magnitudes of the vectors is unity, and the sum of their angles with the reference direction is zero. Thus the planar product of a pair of unit vectors in the reference direction is a third unit vector in the reference direction. This result is written

$$\mathbf{i}^2 = \mathbf{i}. \tag{1.43}$$

Next let us consider the planar product of a unit vector in the reference direction and a unit vector in the quadrature direction. From Eqs. (1.41) and (1.42), the product of the magnitudes of the vectors is unity, and the sum of their angles is $\frac{1}{2}\pi$. Hence, the planar product of unit vectors in the reference and quadrature directions is a unit vector in the quadrature direction. This result is written

$$\mathbf{ij} = \mathbf{j}. \tag{1.44}$$

Let us now consider a pair of unit vectors both pointing in the quadrature direction, and let us form their planar product. From Eq. (1.42), the product of the magnitudes of the vectors is unity, and the sum of their angles is π. Thus the planar product of a pair of unit vectors in the quadrature direction is a unit vector making an angle π with the reference direction and therefore pointing in the direction opposite to the reference direction. This result is written

$$\mathbf{j}^2 = -\mathbf{i}. \tag{1.45}$$

This equation arises from the fact that each of the unit vectors on the left-hand side of Eq. (1.45) makes an angle $\frac{1}{2}\pi$ with the reference direction, so that in forming the planar product in accordance with Eq. (1.25) the two angles $\frac{1}{2}\pi$ are added together, and we have a unit vector pointing in the direction of the negative x axis in Fig. 1.10.

A vector **A**, whose reference component is A_x and whose quadrature component is A_y, may be written

$$\mathbf{A} = A_x\mathbf{i} + A_y\mathbf{j}. \tag{1.46}$$

Likewise a vector **B**, whose reference component is B_x and whose quadrature component is B_y, may be written

$$\mathbf{B} = B_x\mathbf{i} + B_y\mathbf{j}. \tag{1.47}$$

Let us now form the planar product of the two vectors given by Eqs. (1.46) and (1.47). This may be written

$$\mathbf{AB} = (A_x\mathbf{i} + A_y\mathbf{j})(B_x\mathbf{i} + B_y\mathbf{j}) \tag{1.48}$$

and on multiplying out we obtain

$$\mathbf{AB} = A_xB_x\mathbf{i}^2 + (A_xB_y + A_yB_x)\mathbf{ij} + A_yB_y\mathbf{j}^2. \tag{1.49}$$

If in this equation we substitute for the planar products $\mathbf{i}^2$, $\mathbf{ij}$, and $\mathbf{j}^2$ from Eqs. (1.43), (1.44), and (1.45), we obtain

$$\mathbf{AB} = (A_xB_x - A_yB_y)\mathbf{i} + (A_xB_y + A_yB_x)\mathbf{j}. \tag{1.50}$$

We thus see that the Cartesian components of the vector **AB** are

$$A_xB_x - A_yB_y \tag{1.51}$$

for the reference component and

$$A_xB_y + A_yB_x \tag{1.52}$$

for the quadrature component. Expressions (1.51) and (1.52) are therefore the reference and quadrature components of a vector whose magnitude is the product of the magnitudes of the vectors **A** and **B** and whose counterclockwise angle with the reference direction is the sum of the counterclockwise angles for the vectors **A** and **B**.

In calculations of the above type a contracted notation is normally employed. Planar multiplication of any vector by **i** leaves the vector unaffected both in magnitude and direction, and in this sense **i** has the properties of unity. This is illustrated in Eq. (1.44), where planar multiplication of **j** by **i** leaves **j** unaffected. The fact that the unit vector **i** in the reference direction has the algebraic properties of unity is further illustrated in Eq. (1.43), which states that the planear product of **i** with itself is **i**. No confusion is caused if the unit vector **i** in the reference direction is replaced by unity and omitted when multiplied by another quantity. In this contracted notation the reference component of a vector is that part of the Cartesian expression for the vector that is not multiplied by **j**, while the quadrature component of the vector is the part that is multiplied by **j**. In the contracted notation, Eqs. (1.46) and (1.47) are written

$$\mathbf{A} = A_x + \mathbf{j}A_y \tag{1.53}$$

and

$$\mathbf{B} = B_x + \mathbf{j}B_y\,. \tag{1.54}$$

Equation (1.50) giving the planar product of these two vectors, if written in the contracted notation, becomes

$$\mathbf{AB} = (A_xB_x - A_yB_y) + \mathbf{j}(A_xB_y + A_yB_x). \tag{1.55}$$

Furthermore in the contracted notation Eqs. (1.43) and (1.44) become trivial, while Eq. (1.45) becomes

$$\mathbf{j}^2 = -1. \tag{1.56}$$

In the contracted notation the process of forming the planar product of the vector in Eq. (1.53) with the vector in Eq. (1.54) is one of multiplying out to obtain

$$\mathbf{AB} = A_xB_x + (A_xB_y + A_yB_x)\mathbf{j} + A_yB_y\mathbf{j}^2 \tag{1.57}$$

and then replacing $\mathbf{j}^2$ by -1, in accordance with Eq. (1.56), thereby obtained Eq. (1.55).

It will be to our advantage to use the contracted notation. However, it will not be to our immediate advantage to make an additional modification normally adopted by mathematicians. The additional modification involves the omission of the vector symbolism. De-emphasis of the vector character of the quantities employed is the reverse of what is required to understand oscillation theory. We shall therefore retain the vector symbolism but adopt the contracted notation of replacing the unit vector **i** in the reference direction by unity and omitting it when multiplied by another quantity.

It is by adopting the contracted notation and in addition suppressing the vector symbolism that mathematicians arrive at what are called "complex numbers." The relation between the terminology of vectors that we are employing and the terminology of complex numbers is indicated in the table.

THE RELATION BETWEEN THE TERMINOLOGY OF VECTORS AND THE TERMINOLOGY OF COMPLEX NUMBERS

Vector terminology	Complex number terminology
Vector whose Cartesian components are (A_x, A_y)	Complex number $A_x + jA_y$
Reference component of vector	Real part of complex number
Quadrature component of vector	Imaginary part of complex number
Magnitude of vector	Modulus of complex number
Counterclockwise angle of vector	Argument of complex number

It is particularly to be noticed that Eq. (1.56) has nothing to do with finding the arithmetical square root of -1. There is no such concept as the arithmetical square root of -1. Equation (1.56) is the contracted form of Eq. (1.45) which states that, if we turn to the left through a right angle, and then repeat the operation, we are facing backwards.

Equation (1.56) may, if desired, be rewritten in the form

$$\sqrt{-1} = \pm \mathbf{j}. \tag{1.58}$$

If this is done it must be clearly understood from Eq. (1.45) that Eq. (1.58) is the contracted form of the equation

$$\sqrt{-\mathbf{i}} = \pm \mathbf{j}. \tag{1.59}$$

The significance of this equation is illustrated in Fig 1.9(b) if the magnitude of the vector **A** is unity. Equations (1.58) and (1.59) convey the information that the planar product of $+\mathbf{j}$ with itself, and of $-\mathbf{j}$ with itself, is a unit vector in the direction opposite to the reference direction. If we turn through a right-angle, either to the left or to the right, and then repeat the operation, we are facing backwards.

1.7. The Quotient of Two Vectors in Cartesian Components

Suppose that a vector **A** has Cartesian components (A_x, A_y) and a vector **B** has Cartesian components (B_x, B_y). In contracted notation the two vectors are then represented as shown in Eqs. (1.53) and (1.54), and their planar product is given by Eq. (1.55). Let us now suppose that it is required to calculate the Cartesian components of the vector formed by taking the quotient of **A** by **B**. In other words we require the reference and quadrature components of the vector

$$\frac{\mathbf{A}}{\mathbf{B}} = \frac{A_x + \mathbf{j}A_y}{B_x + \mathbf{j}B_y}. \tag{1.60}$$

To achieve this we form the planar product of both the numerator and denominator of the right-hand side of Eq. (1.60) with the vector

$$B_x - \mathbf{j}B_y. \tag{1.61}$$

We thus obtain

$$\frac{\mathbf{A}}{\mathbf{B}} = \frac{(A_x + \mathbf{j}A_y)(B_x - \mathbf{j}B_y)}{(B_x + \mathbf{j}B_y)(B_x - \mathbf{j}B_y)}. \tag{1.62}$$

We now multiply out the numerator and denominator using the contracted equation (1.56), thereby obtaining

$$\frac{\mathbf{A}}{\mathbf{B}} = \frac{(A_xB_x + A_yB_y) + \mathbf{j}(A_yB_x - A_xB_y)}{B_x^2 + B_y^2}. \tag{1.63}$$

It then follows that the reference component of the vector **A/B** is

$$\frac{A_x B_x + A_y B_y}{B_x^2 + B_y^2} \tag{1.64}$$

and the quadrature component is

$$\frac{A_y B_x - A_x B_y}{B_x^2 + B_y^2}. \tag{1.65}$$

1.8. The Role to Be Played by Vector Algebra in Oscillation Analysis

In this chapter we have seen that:

(i) a sinusoidal oscillation of angular frequency ω is conveniently thought of as the component in the reference direction of a vector rotating with uniform angular velocity ω,

(ii) two or more oscillations are conveniently added or subtracted by vector addition or subtraction of the associated rotating vectors,

(iii) two oscillations of the same frequency are conveniently compared in amplitude and phase by taking the quotient of the associated rotating vectors as defined in Section 1.3, and

(iv) in exploiting these vector ideas, it is convenient to introduce the concept of planar product, which is the process that undoes the quotient operation defined in Section 1.3.

Summarizing Exercises

1.1. Explain how a sinusoidal oscillation may be represented as the component along a reference direction of a rotating vector. In terms of the rotating vector explain what is meant by the amplitude, the phase, and the angular frequency of the oscillation.

1.2. Explain how the addition and subtraction of sinusoidal oscillations may be achieved by a vector method. If two sinusoidal oscillations of the same angular frequency ω have amplitudes A, B and phases α, β, respectively, show vectorially that their sum is a sinusoidal oscillation of angular frequency ω, and describe a vector method for evaluating the amplitude and phase of the resultant oscillation.

1.3. If a number of sinusoidal oscillations all have the same angular frequency, explain how their amplitudes and phases may be exhibited in a vector diagram in which the vectors do not rotate.

1.4. State what is meant by the quotient of two vectors. Explain how the quotient of two vectors may be used to compare the amplitudes and phases of two sinusoidal oscillations of the same angular frequency.

1.5. Explain what is meant by the planar product of two vectors. Show that, if the planar product of a vector **A** with a vector **B** gives a vector **C**, then the quotient of **C** by **B** gives **A**, and the quotient of **C** by **A** gives **B**.

1.6. Explain what is meant by the square root of a given vector, showing that there are two square-root vectors. Draw diagrams to illustrate the process of forming the square root of a vector (a) when the given vector points in an arbitrary direction, (b) when the given vector points in the reference direction, and (c) when the given vector points in the direction opposite to the reference direction.

1.7. Explain what is meant by the quadrature direction. Evaluate the planar product of (a) a unit vector **i** in the reference direction with itself, (b) a unit vector **i** in the reference direction with a unit vector **j** in the quadrature direction, and (c) a unit vector **j** in the quadrature direction with itself.

1.8. Show that the planar product of a vector whose components in the reference and quadrature directions are (A_x, A_y) with a vector whose components are (B_x, B_y)

is a vector whose components are $(A_x B_x - A_y B_y, A_x B_y + A_y B_x)$.

1.9. Explain why it is feasible and convenient, when dealing with planar products and quotients of vectors, to employ a contracted notation in which the unit vector **i** in the reference direction is replaced by unity and omitted when multiplied by another quantity.

1.10. Describe carefully the significance of the equation $\mathbf{j} = \sqrt{-1}$.

1.11. Describe the relation between the terminology of vector analysis and the terminology of complex numbers.

1.12. A vector **A** has reference and quadrature components (A_x, A_y) and a second vector **B** has components (B_x, B_y). Calculate the components of the vector **A**/**B**.

CHAPTER 2

VECTOR ALGEBRA USING PLANAR PRODUCTS AND QUOTIENTS

2.1. Introduction

In the previous chapter we saw how to make use of vector concepts in the handling of sinusoidal oscillations. In oscillation analysis tremendous use is made of the processes of vector addition, vector subtraction, planar product, and vector quotient, which were introduced in Chapter 1. We must now develop the associated vector algebra in order to be able to handle adequately the oscillatory behavior of systems encountered in physics and engineering. In this chapter we shall examine the significance of expressions of the form

$$\frac{(\mathbf{s} - \mathbf{s}_1')(\mathbf{s} - \mathbf{s}_2') \cdots (\mathbf{s} - \mathbf{s}_m')}{(\mathbf{s} - \mathbf{s}_1)(\mathbf{s} - \mathbf{s}_2) \cdots (\mathbf{s} - \mathbf{s}_n)} \tag{2.1}$$

when $\mathbf{s}_1, \mathbf{s}_2, \ldots, \mathbf{s}_n; \mathbf{s}_1', \mathbf{s}_2', \ldots, \mathbf{s}_m'$ are fixed vectors, and $\mathbf{s}$ is a vector that is variable in magnitude and direction.

2.2. Algebraic Functions of a Vector

Expression (2.1) involves, both in the numerator and in the denominator, linear factors of the form

$$\mathbf{s} - \mathbf{s}_0 \tag{2.2}$$

where $\mathbf{s}_0$ is a fixed vector and $\mathbf{s}$ is a variable vector. The significance of expression (2.2) is illustrated in Fig. 2.1. The vector given by expression (2.2) runs from the tip of the fixed vector $\mathbf{s}_0$ to the tip of the variable vector $\mathbf{s}$. As the vector $\mathbf{s}$ varies in magnitude and direction, it can easily be seen from Fig. 2.1 how the vector $\mathbf{s} - \mathbf{s}_0$ varies in magnitude and direction.

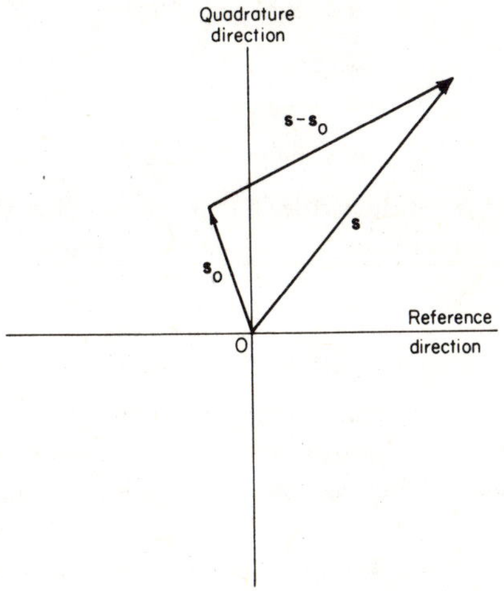

FIG. 2.1. Illustrating subtraction of a fixed vector $\mathbf{s}_0$ from a variable vector $\mathbf{s}$.

By means of diagrams such as that shown in Fig. 2.1 we may understand the vector significance of each of the factors in the denominator of expression (2.1). From the individual vectors $\mathbf{s} - \mathbf{s}_1$, $\mathbf{s} - \mathbf{s}_2$, ..., $\mathbf{s} - \mathbf{s}_n$ we then formulate the planar product

$$(\mathbf{s} - \mathbf{s}_1)(\mathbf{s} - \mathbf{s}_2) \cdots (\mathbf{s} - \mathbf{s}_n). \tag{2.3}$$

Evaluation of this planar product yields a vector $\mathbf{P}$ the magnitude and direction of which vary as we vary the magnitude and direction of $\mathbf{s}$. We therefore write

$$\mathbf{P}(\mathbf{s}) = (\mathbf{s} - \mathbf{s}_1)(\mathbf{s} - \mathbf{s}_2) \cdots (\mathbf{s} - \mathbf{s}_n). \tag{2.4}$$

The calculation of the magnitude and direction of the vector **P** for any selected magnitude and direction of **s** may be described as follows: By means of diagrams such as that shown in Fig. 2.1 we evaluate the magnitude and direction of each of the vectors corresponding to the factors on the right-hand side of Eq. (2.4). Let us suppose that, in this way, we have evaluated the various factors as follows:

$$\begin{aligned} \mathbf{s} - \mathbf{s}_1 &= r_1 \angle \theta_1 \\ \mathbf{s} - \mathbf{s}_2 &= r_2 \angle \theta_2 \\ &\cdots\cdots\cdots \\ \mathbf{s} - \mathbf{s}_n &= r_n \angle \theta_n \, . \end{aligned} \tag{2.5}$$

From the planar product rule it then follows that the magnitude of **P** is the product of the magnitudes the vectors given in Eqs. (2.5) so that

$$|\mathbf{P}| = r_1 r_2 \cdots r_n \, . \tag{2.6}$$

Likewise, from the planar product rule, it follows that the counterclockwise angle of the vector **P** is the sum of the counterclockwise angles of the vectors given in Eqs. (2.5). This means that

$$\angle \mathbf{P} = \theta_1 + \theta_2 + \cdots \theta_n \, . \tag{2.7}$$

Thus the vector **P** defined by Eq. (2.4) is obtained by multiplying the magnitudes and adding the angles of the vectors given in Eqs. (2.5).

The result described by Eqs. (2.6) and (2.7) is conveniently represented graphically as shown in Fig. 2.2. The vectors $\mathbf{s}_1, \mathbf{s}_2, \ldots, \mathbf{s}_n$ run from the origin O to the points labeled $\mathbf{s}_1, \mathbf{s}_2, \ldots, \mathbf{s}_n$ and indicated by crosses. The vectors $\mathbf{s}_1, \mathbf{s}_2, \ldots, \mathbf{s}_n$ are indicated in Fig. 2.2 only by the positions of their tips. In each case the vector is to be pictured as drawn from the origin to the point designated as the tip of the vector. The tips of the vectors $\mathbf{s}_1, \mathbf{s}_2, \ldots, \mathbf{s}_n$ are often described as the "points" $\mathbf{s}_1, \mathbf{s}_2, \ldots, \mathbf{s}_n$. In the same way there is shown in Fig. 2.2 the "point" **s**. This means that the vector **s** appearing on the right-hand side of Eq. (2.4) is represented in Fig. 2.2 by a vector drawn from the origin O to the point labeled $\mathbf{s}$. Using Fig. 2.1 we can now see that the vector corresponding to the factor $\mathbf{s} - \mathbf{s}_1$ on the right-hand side of Eq. (2.4) is the vector running from the point $\mathbf{s}_1$ to the point $\mathbf{s}$ in Fig. 2.2. Likewise the vector corresponding to the factor $\mathbf{s} - \mathbf{s}_2$ is the vector running from the point $\mathbf{s}_2$ to the point $\mathbf{s}$, and so on. Equation (2.6) therefore states that the vector $\mathbf{P}$ defined by Eq. (2.4) has a magnitude

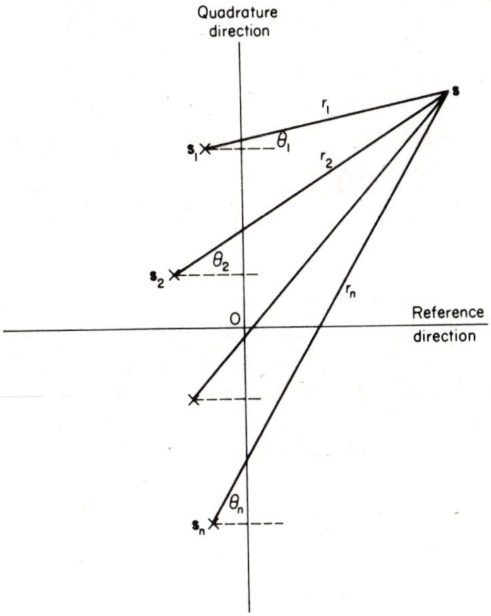

FIG. 2.2. Illustrating calculation of the vector $\mathbf{P}(\mathbf{s})$ given by Eq. (2.4).

equal to the product of the distances of the point $\mathbf{s}$ from the points $\mathbf{s}_1, \mathbf{s}_2, ..., \mathbf{s}_n$, while Eq. (2.7) states that the counterclockwise angle of the vector $\mathbf{P}$ is the sum of the angles $\theta_1, \theta_2, ..., \theta_n$ appearing in Fig. 2.2. Thus, by means of Eqs. (2.6) and (2.7) together with Fig. 2.2, we can see how the magnitude and direction of the vector $\mathbf{P}(\mathbf{s})$ defined by Eq. (2.4) varies with the magnitude and direction of the vector $\mathbf{s}$.

The method that we have used for investigating the significance of the denominator in expression (2.1) may equally well be used for the numerator. The numerator is a vector **N** that is derived by planar multiplication of the vectors $\mathbf{s} - \mathbf{s}_1'$, $\mathbf{s} - \mathbf{s}_2'$, ..., $\mathbf{s} - \mathbf{s}_m'$. If $\mathbf{s}_1'$, $\mathbf{s}_2'$, ..., $\mathbf{s}_m'$ are fixed vectors and **s** is a vector that is variable in magnitude and direction, then **N** is a vector whose magnitude and direction depend on the magnitude and direction of **s**. This is written

$$\mathbf{N}(\mathbf{s}) = (\mathbf{s} - \mathbf{s}_1')(\mathbf{s} - \mathbf{s}_2') \cdots (\mathbf{s} - \mathbf{s}_m'). \tag{2.8}$$

The vectors corresponding to the individual factors on the right-hand side of Eq. (2.8) may be calculated by the method illustrated in Fig. 2.1. Let us suppose that the magnitudes and directions of these factors have been evaluated with the results:

$$\begin{aligned} \mathbf{s} - \mathbf{s}_1' &= r_1' \angle\theta_1' \\ \mathbf{s} - \mathbf{s}_2' &= r_2' \angle\theta_2' \\ &\cdots\cdots\cdots\cdots \\ \mathbf{s} - \mathbf{s}_m' &= r_m' \angle\theta_m'. \end{aligned} \tag{2.9}$$

Then it follows from the planar product rule that

$$|\mathbf{N}| = r_1' r_2' \cdots r_m' \tag{2.10}$$

and

$$\angle\mathbf{N} = \theta_1' + \theta_2' + \cdots \theta_m'. \tag{2.11}$$

The significance of Eqs. (2.10) and (2.11) may be illustrated graphically as shown in Fig. 2.3. Equations (2.10) and (2.11), together with Fig. 2.3, show how the magnitude and direction of the vector **N**(**s**) depend on the magnitude and direction of **s**.

The complete expression (2.1) is now obtained by forming the quotient of the vector **N**(**s**) defined by Eq. (2.8) by the vector **P**(**s**) defined by Eq. (2.4). If formation of this quotient leads to a vector **F**, we may write

$$\mathbf{F}(\mathbf{s}) = \frac{(\mathbf{s} - \mathbf{s}_1')(\mathbf{s} - \mathbf{s}_2') \cdots (\mathbf{s} - \mathbf{s}_m')}{(\mathbf{s} - \mathbf{s}_1)(\mathbf{s} - \mathbf{s}_2) \cdots (\mathbf{s} - \mathbf{s}_n)} \tag{2.12}$$

and this is a vector the magnitude and direction of which vary with the magnitude and direction of **s**. Equation (2.12) may be written

$$\mathbf{F}(\mathbf{s}) = \frac{\mathbf{N}(\mathbf{s})}{\mathbf{P}(\mathbf{s})} \tag{2.13}$$

from which it follows that

$$|\,\mathbf{F}\,| = \frac{|\,\mathbf{N}\,|}{|\,\mathbf{P}\,|} \tag{2.14}$$

and

$$\angle\mathbf{F} = \angle\mathbf{N} - \angle\mathbf{P}. \tag{2.15}$$

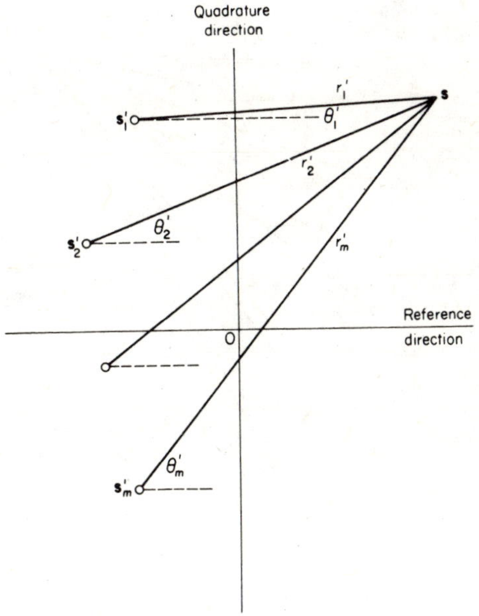

FIG. 2.3. Illustrating calculation of the vector **N**(**s**) given by Eq. (2.8).

Substitution from Eqs. (2.6), (2.7), (2.10) and (2.11) into Eqs. (2.14) and (2.15) gives

$$|\,\mathbf{F}\,| = \frac{r_1'r_2' \cdots r_m'}{r_1r_2 \cdots r_n} \tag{2.16}$$

and

$$\angle\mathbf{F} = (\theta_1' + \theta_2' + \cdots + \theta_m') - (\theta_1 + \theta_2 + \cdots \theta_n). \tag{2.17}$$

The significance of Eqs. (2.16) and (2.17) may be illustrated graphically with the aid of Fig. 2.4. Here the point P is the tip of the vector $\mathbf{s}$ drawn from the origin O, so that $\mathbf{s} = \overrightarrow{OP}$. The crosses are the points $\mathbf{s}_1$, $\mathbf{s}_2$, ..., $\mathbf{s}_n$ taken from Fig. 2.2, and the circles are the points $\mathbf{s}_1'$, $\mathbf{s}_2'$ ..., $\mathbf{s}_m'$ taken from Fig. 2.3. Thus the vectors drawn from the circles in Fig. 2.4 to the point $\mathbf{s}$ are the

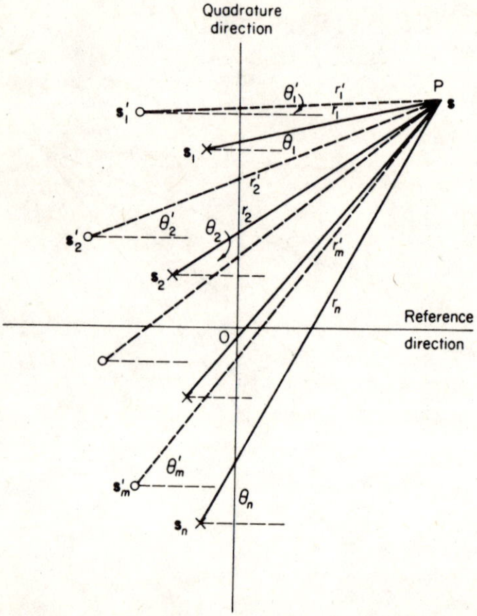

FIG. 2.4. Illustrating calculation of the vector $\mathbf{F}(\mathbf{s})$ given by Eq. (2.12).

factors in the numerator on the right-hand side of Eq. (2.12), while the vectors drawn from the crosses in Fig. 2.4 to the point $\mathbf{s}$ are the factors in the denominator of the expression on the right-hand of Eq. (2.12). Equation (2.16) states that the magnitude of the vector $\mathbf{F}$ given by Eq. (2.12) is the product of the distances of the point $\mathbf{s}$ from the circles in Fig. 2.4 divided by the product of the distances of the point $\mathbf{s}$ from the crosses. Likewise Eq. (2.17) states that the counterclockwise angle of the vector $\mathbf{F}$ is obtained by taking the sum of the angles $\theta_1', \theta_2', ..., \theta_m'$ in Fig. 2.4 and subtracting the sum of the angle $\theta_1, \theta_2, ..., \theta_n$. Thus, Eqs. (2.16) and (2.17), together with Fig. 2.4, illustrate how the magnitude and direction of the vector **F**(**s**) defined by Eq. (2.12) vary with magnitude and direction of **s**.

If the vector **s** coincides with the vector $\mathbf{s}_1'$ in Eq. (2.12), the magnitude of **F** is zero; in Fig. 2.4 the point **s** then coincides with the point $\mathbf{s}_1'$, the distance r_1' is zero, and consequently the magnitude of the vector **F** is zero in accordance with Eq. (2.16). In the same way, if the point **s** coincides with the point $\mathbf{s}_2'$, the magnitude of **F** is zero. If the vector **s** coincides with any of the points indicated by circles in Fig. 2.4, the magnitude of **F** is zero. For this reason the points $\mathbf{s}_1', \mathbf{s}_2', ..., \mathbf{s}_m'$ are referred to as the "zeros" of the expression on the right-hand side of Eq. (2.12). If the point **s** coincides with any of the zero's, one of the factors in the numerator on the right-hand side of Eq. (2.12) is zero, and consequently the vector **F** vanishes.

If in Fig. 2.4 the point **s** approaches the point $\mathbf{s}_1$, the distance r_1 tends to zero, and consequently the magnitude of the vector **F** becomes indefinitely large in accordance with Eq. (2.16). This may also be expressed by saying that, as **s** tends to $\mathbf{s}_1$ in Eq. (2.12), the magnitude of the vector **F** tends to infinity. Likewise, if the point **s** in Fig. 2.4 tends to any of the points marked by crosses, the magnitude of the vector **F** tends to infinity, because one of the factors in the denominator on the right-hand side of Eq. (2.12) tends to zero. The points indicated by crosses in Fig. 2.4 are referred to as the "poles" of the expression on the right-hand side of Eq. (2.12). Each pole corresponds to the vanishing of one of the factors in the denominator of the expression on the right-hand side of Eq. (2.12).

If two of the points $\mathbf{s}_1, \mathbf{s}_2, ..., \mathbf{s}_n$ have identical positions in Fig. 2.4, then two of the factors in the denominator on the right-hand side of Eq. (2.12) are identical. This gives what is known as a double pole. In the same way, if two of the factors in the numerator on the right-hand side of Eq. (2.12) are identical, we have a double zero. Multiple poles and zeros of higher orders can also occur. However, it will be assumed unless otherwise stated that all poles are simple poles and all zeros are simple zeros.

The poles and zeros of a vector-algebraic function of **s**, such as that on the right-hand side of Eq. (2.12), are extremely important. The poles $\mathbf{s}_1$, $\mathbf{s}_2$, ..., $\mathbf{s}_n$ give the vectors **s** for which the magnitude of the vector **F** is indefinitely large. The zeros $\mathbf{s}_1'$, $\mathbf{s}_2'$, ..., $\mathbf{s}_m'$ give the vectors **s** for which the magnitude of the vector **F** is indefinitely small. Knowledge of the poles and zeros specifies the function on the right-hand side of Eq. (2.12). If we know the positions of the poles and zeros in Fig. 2.4, we may join them to the tip of any specified vector **s** and then use Eqs. (2.16) and (2.17) to evaluate the magnitude and direction of the vector **F**(**s**) defined by Eq. (2.12).

As an example, let us consider the vector

$$\mathbf{F}(\mathbf{s}) = \frac{(\mathbf{s} - \mathbf{s}_1')(\mathbf{s} - \mathbf{s}_2')}{(\mathbf{s} - \mathbf{s}_1)(\mathbf{s} - \mathbf{s}_2)} \tag{2.18}$$

in the circumstances when

$$\mathbf{s}_1 = -3, \qquad \mathbf{s}_2 = -4 \tag{2.19}$$

$$\mathbf{s}_1' = -1, \qquad \mathbf{s}_2' = -2. \tag{2.20}$$

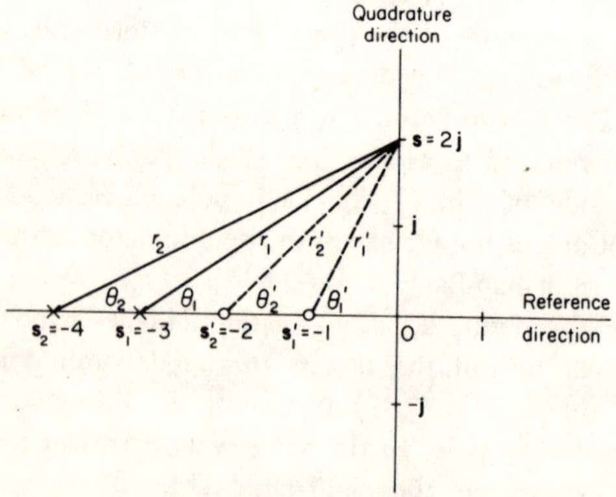

FIG. 2.5. Illustrating calculation of the vector **F** given by Eq. (2.18) under the circumstances described by Eqs. (2.19), (2.20), and (2.21).

Let us evaluate the magnitude and direction of **F**(**s**) when

$$\mathbf{s} = 2\mathbf{j}. \tag{2.21}$$

In these circumstances Fig. 2.4 takes the form shown in Fig. 2.5. The poles of the expression on the right-hand side of Eq. (2.18) are given by Eqs. (2.19) and are indicated by the crosses in Fig. 2.5. The zeros of the expression on the right-hand side of Eq. (2.18) are given by Eqs. (2.20) and are represented by the circles in Fig. 2.5. The vector **s** for which we are to evaluate the vector **F**(**s**) is given by Eq. (2.21) and has its tip at distance 2 along the positive quadrature axis. From the geometry of Fig. 2.5 we deduce that

$$\begin{aligned} r_1 &= \sqrt{13} & \theta_1 &= \tan^{-1}\tfrac{2}{3} \\ r_2 &= 2\sqrt{5} & \theta_2 &= \tan^{-1}\tfrac{1}{2} \\ r_1' &= \sqrt{5} & \theta_1' &= \tan^{-1}2 \\ r_2' &= 2\sqrt{2} & \theta_2' &= \tfrac{1}{4}\pi. \end{aligned} \tag{2.22}$$

From Eqs. (2.22) we deduce that [cf. Eqs. (2.16) and (2.17)]

$$|\mathbf{F}| = \frac{\sqrt{5}\cdot 2\sqrt{2}}{\sqrt{13}\cdot 2\sqrt{5}} \tag{2.23}$$

and

$$\angle\mathbf{F} = (\tan^{-1}2 + \tfrac{1}{4}\pi) - (\tan^{-1}\tfrac{2}{3} + \tan^{-1}\tfrac{1}{2}). \tag{2.24}$$

It follows that the required vector is

$$\mathbf{F} = 0.392 \angle 48.^\circ1. \tag{2.25}$$

As a further example, let us again consider the vector **F**(**s**) defined by Eq. (2.18), but let us now suppose that

$$\mathbf{s}_1 = -2 + \mathbf{j} \qquad \mathbf{s}_2 = -2 - \mathbf{j} \tag{2.26}$$

$$\mathbf{s}_1' = -1 + 2j \qquad \mathbf{s}_2' = -1 - 2\mathbf{j}. \tag{2.27}$$

If we again suppose that **s** is given by Eq. (2.21), Fig. 2.4 takes the form shown in Fig. 2.6. We now derive from the geometry of Fig. 2.6 the values

$$\begin{aligned} r_1 &= \sqrt{5} & \theta_1 &= \tan^{-1}\tfrac{1}{2} \\ r_2 &= \sqrt{13} & \theta_2 &= \tan^{-1}\tfrac{3}{2} \\ r_1' &= 1 & \theta_1' &= 0 \\ r_2' &= \sqrt{17} & \theta_2' &= \tan^{-1}4. \end{aligned} \tag{2.28}$$

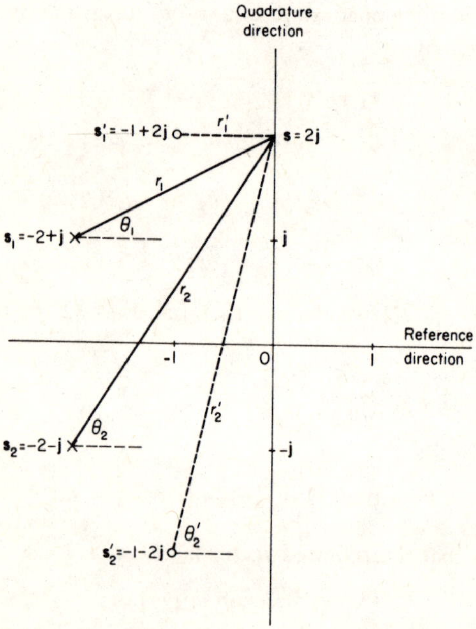

FIG. 2.6. Illustrating calculation of the vector **F** given by Eq. (2.18) under the circumstances described by Eqs. (2.21), (2.26), and (2.27).

From Eqs. (2.28) we deduce that [cf. Eqs. (2.16) and (2.17)]

$$|\mathbf{F}| = \frac{1}{\sqrt{5}} \frac{\sqrt{17}}{\sqrt{13}} \tag{2.29}$$

and

$$\angle \mathbf{F} = (0 + \tan^{-1}4) - (\tan^{-1}\tfrac{1}{2} + \tan^{-1}\tfrac{3}{2}) \qquad (2.30)$$

from which it follows that

$$\mathbf{F} = 0.511 \angle -6.^\circ 9. \qquad (2.31)$$

2.3. Polynominal Functions of a Vector

A polynominal function of a vector **s** of degree n is defined by the equation

$$\mathbf{P}(\mathbf{s}) = \mathbf{a}_0 + \mathbf{a}_1\mathbf{s} + \cdots + \mathbf{a}_n\mathbf{s}^n \qquad (2.32)$$

where $\mathbf{a}_0, \mathbf{a}_1, ..., \mathbf{a}_n$ are fixed vectors and **s** is a vector that may be varied in magnitude and direction. All products involved in Eq. (2.32) are planar products. The expression on the right-hand side of Eq. (2.4), if multiplied out, is a polynominal function of **s** of degree n; in this case the coefficient $\mathbf{a}_n$ is a unit vector in the reference direction. Thus the numerator and denominator of the expression on the right-hand side of Eq. (2.12) are polynominal functions of **s**, the numerator being of degree m and the denominator of degree n.

The significance to be attached to the polynominal function of **s** defined by Eq. (2.32) may be described as follows: We suppose that the vector coefficients $\mathbf{a}_0, \mathbf{a}_1, ..., \mathbf{a}_m$ are prescribed in magnitude and direction. Now select a magnitude and direction for the vector **s**. By the planar product rule we then evaluate in magnitude and direction the vectors $\mathbf{a}_1\mathbf{s}, \mathbf{a}_2\mathbf{s}^2, ..., \mathbf{a}_n\mathbf{s}^n$. We then know in magnitude and direction the vector corresponding to each term on the right-hand side of Eq. (2.32), and application of the rule for vector addition now gives the magnitude and direction of the vector **P**. This process may be repeated for any number of magnitudes and directions of the vector **s**, thereby describing **P** as a function of **s**.

Let us illustrate the process for evaluating a polynominal function of a vector by using the polynominal of the first degree defined

$$\mathbf{P}(\mathbf{s}) = \mathbf{a}_0 + \mathbf{a}_1\mathbf{s} \qquad (2.33)$$

where

$$\mathbf{a}_0 = 1 \angle \frac{\pi}{12} \tag{2.34}$$

$$\mathbf{a}_1 = 2 \angle \frac{5\pi}{12} . \tag{2.35}$$

Let us evaluate the vector **P** defined by these equations when

$$\mathbf{s} = \frac{1}{2} \angle \frac{\pi}{3} . \tag{2.36}$$

The vector **s** defined by Eq. (2.36) is illustrated in Fig. 2.7(a).

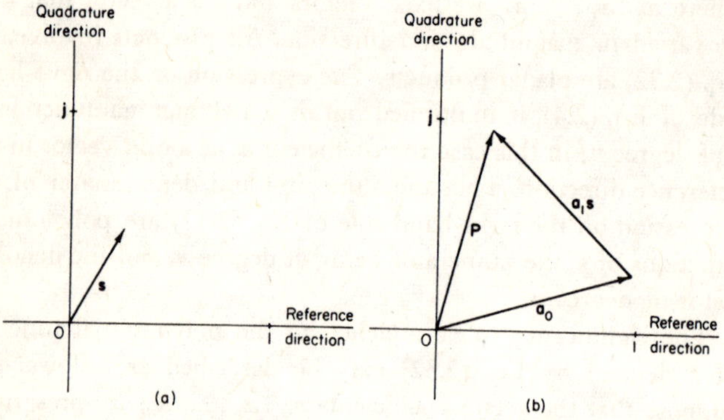

FIG. 2.7. Illustrating calculation of the vector **F** from the vector **s** in accordance with Eq. (2.33).

To evaluate for this vector the corresponding vector **P** given by Eq. (2.33) we have to add the vectors $\mathbf{a}_0$ and $\mathbf{a}_1\mathbf{s}$. The first of these is given by Eq. (2.34) and is illustrated in Fig. 2.7(b), while the second is obtained by performing the planar product of the vectors given in Eqs. (2.35) and (2.36), and is therefore

$$\mathbf{a}_1\mathbf{s} = 1 \angle \frac{3\pi}{4} . \tag{2.37}$$

In Fig. 2.7(b) are illustrated the vectors $\mathbf{a}_0$ and $\mathbf{a}_1\mathbf{s}$ from Eqs.

(2.34) and (2.37) together with their vector sum, which evaluates to

$$\mathbf{P} = 1 \angle \frac{5\pi}{12}. \tag{2.38}$$

If the magnitude and direction of the vector $\mathbf{s}$ in Fig. 2.7(a) were varied, a corresponding variation would occur in the magnitude and direction of the vector $\mathbf{a}_1\mathbf{s}$ in Fig. 2.7(b), and consequently in the resultant vector $\mathbf{P}$. In this way we can calculate for the vector $\mathbf{P}$ defined by Eqs. (2.33), (2.34), and (2.35) the way in which its magnitude and direction vary with the magnitude and direction of $\mathbf{s}$.

As another example of a polynominal function of a vector let us consider the quadratic polynominal defined by

$$\mathbf{P}(\mathbf{s}) = \mathbf{a}_0 + \mathbf{a}_1\mathbf{s} + \mathbf{a}_2\mathbf{s}^2 \tag{2.39}$$

where

$$\mathbf{a}_0 = 1 \angle \frac{\pi}{12} \tag{2.40}$$

$$\mathbf{a}_1 = \sqrt{2} \angle \frac{\pi}{6} \tag{2.41}$$

$$\mathbf{a}_2 = 2\sqrt{2} \angle \frac{\pi}{3}. \tag{2.42}$$

Let us evaluate the magnitude and direction of the vector $\mathbf{P}$ defined by these equations when the vector $\mathbf{s}$ is given by

$$\mathbf{s} = \frac{1}{2} \angle \frac{\pi}{3} \tag{2.43}$$

as illustrated in Fig. 2.8(a). To evaluate the vector on the right-hand side of Eq. (2.39) we shall need to evaluate the vector $\mathbf{s}^2$. Application of the planar product rule to Eq. (2.43) gives

$$\mathbf{s}^2 = \frac{1}{4} \angle \frac{2\pi}{3} \tag{2.44}$$

and this vector is also illustrated in Fig. 2.8(a). The vector addition involved on the right-hand side of Eq. (2.39) is illustrated in Fig. 2.8(b). The second term involves the planar product of the vector $\mathbf{a}_1$ given by Eq. (2.41) and the vector $\mathbf{s}$ given by Eq. (2.43), so that

$$\mathbf{a}_1\mathbf{s} = \frac{1}{\sqrt{2}} \angle \frac{\pi}{2} \tag{2.45}$$

as illustrated in Fig. 2.8(b). The third term on the right-hand side of Eq. (2.39) involves the planar product of the vector $\mathbf{a}_2$ given by Eq. (2.42) and the vector $\mathbf{s}^2$ given by Eq. (2.44), so that

$$\mathbf{a}_2\mathbf{s}^2 = \frac{1}{\sqrt{2}} \angle \pi. \tag{2.46}$$

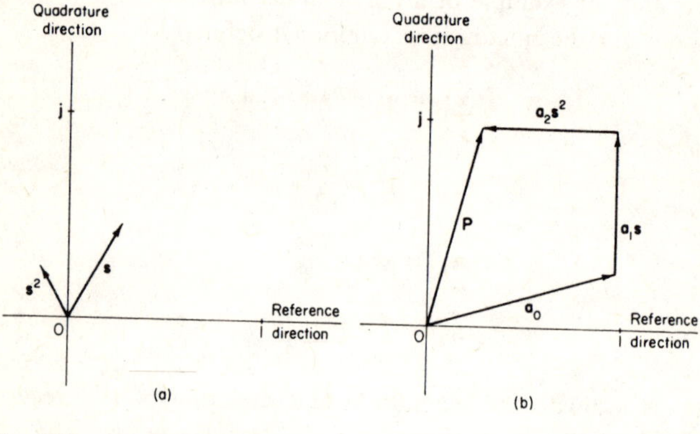

FIG. 2.8. Illustrating calculation of the vector **F** from the vector **s** in accordance with Eq. (2.39).

The vector sum indicated on the right-hand side of Eq. (2.39) must now be calculated as shown in Fig. 2.8(b), leading to the resultant vector

$$\mathbf{P} = 1 \angle \frac{5\pi}{12}. \tag{2.47}$$

This is the vector **P** defined by Eq. (2.39) when the vector coefficients $\mathbf{a}_0$, $\mathbf{a}_1$, and $\mathbf{a}_2$ are given by Eqs. (2.40), (2.41), and (2.42), and the vector **s** has the magnitude and direction given by Eq. (2.43). From Fig. 2.8 we can see that, as the magnitude and direction of **s** in Fig. 2.8(a) vary, so also do the magnitudes and directions of $\mathbf{a}_1\mathbf{s}$ and $\mathbf{a}_2\mathbf{s}^2$ in Fig. 2.8(b), and consequently also the magnitude and direction of the resultant vector **P**. In this way we may follow the functional dependence of **P** upon **s**.

The procedure indicated in Figs. 2.7 and 2.8 may be extended to the polynominal function of **s** of degree *n* in Eq. (2.32). The planar product is used in calculating the magnitudes and directions of the vectors corresponding to each term on the right-hand side of Eq. (2.32), and then vector addition is applied to the terms. As the magnitude and direction of the vector **s** vary, so do the magnitude and direction of the vector **P**, and this constitutes the functional dependence of the **P** on **s**.

2.4. Factorization of Polynomial Functions of a Vector

The problem frequently arises of factorizing a polynomial function of a vector. This involves writing the polynomial function of **s** in Eq. (2.32) in the form

$$\mathbf{P}(\mathbf{s}) = \mathbf{a}_n(\mathbf{s} - \mathbf{s}_1)(\mathbf{s} - \mathbf{s}_2) \cdots (\mathbf{s} - \mathbf{s}_n) \qquad (2.48)$$

where $\mathbf{s}_1, \mathbf{s}_2, \ldots, \mathbf{s}_n$ are fixed vectors. If a polynomial function of **s** can be readily factorized, we can apply the method of evaluation described in connection with Fig. 2.2 in place of that described in connection with Fig. 2.8, and this is especially convenient if **P** has to be studied as a function of **s**. The process of factorizing the polynomial in Eq. (2.32) involves finding the fixed vectors $\mathbf{s}_1, \mathbf{s}_2, \ldots, \mathbf{s}_n$ in Eq. (2.48), and these are the zeros of $\mathbf{P}(\mathbf{s})$. Thus the vectors $\mathbf{s}_1, \mathbf{s}_2, \ldots, \mathbf{s}_n$ may be described as the vector roots of the vector algebraic equation

$$\mathbf{a}_0 + \mathbf{a}_1\mathbf{s} + \cdots + \mathbf{a}_n\mathbf{s}^n = 0. \qquad (2.49)$$

The significance of a vector root of a vector algebraic equation may be illustrated with the aid of the quadratic equation

$$\mathbf{a}_0 + \mathbf{a}_1\mathbf{s} + \mathbf{a}_2\mathbf{s}^2 = 0. \qquad (2.50)$$

The procedure for calculating the vector on the left-hand side of Eq. (2.50) for any assigned magnitude and direction of the vector **s** has been discussed in the previous section and illustrated in Fig. 2.8. The process of solving the quadratic equation (2.50) is one of adjusting the magnitude and direction of the vector **s** in Fig. 2.8(a), so that the resultant vector **P** in Fig. 2.8(b) reduces to zero. The three vectors corresponding to the three terms on the left-hand side of the quadratic equation (2.50) then form a closed triangle.

Evaluation of the vector roots of vector algebraic equations follows the same process involved in finding scalar roots of scalar algebraic equations. It is merely a matter of making systematic use of the sums, differences, planar products, and quotients of vector quantities in place of the sums, differences, products, and quotients of scalar quantities. This may be illustrated by examining the procedure for finding the vector roots of a vector quadratic equation. Let us consider the quadratic equation

$$\mathbf{a}\mathbf{s}^2 + \mathbf{b}\mathbf{s} + \mathbf{c} = 0. \tag{2.51}$$

In this equation **a**, **b**, and **c** are fixed vectors, and **s** is a vector to be determined in magnitude and direction so that the vector on the left-hand side vanishes; all products involved in Eq. (2.51) are planar products. To solve the vector quadratic equation (2.51) we follow the same procedure as in scalar algebra, remembering however that all products are planar products of vectors. First we form the planar product of Eq. (2.51) with the vector **a**, thereby obtaining

$$\mathbf{a}^2\mathbf{s}^2 + \mathbf{a}\mathbf{b}\mathbf{s} + \mathbf{a}\mathbf{c} = 0. \tag{2.52}$$

We now notice that the first two terms on the left-hand side of Eq. (2.52) are two of the terms that occur when multiplying out the expression $(\mathbf{a}\mathbf{s} + \frac{1}{2}\mathbf{b})^2$. Equation (2.52) may therefore be rewritten as

$$(\mathbf{a}\mathbf{s} + \tfrac{1}{2}\mathbf{b})^2 - \tfrac{1}{4}\mathbf{b}^2 + \mathbf{a}\mathbf{c} = 0 \tag{2.53}$$

or alternatively as

$$(\mathbf{a}\mathbf{s} + \tfrac{1}{2}\mathbf{b})^2 = \tfrac{1}{4}(\mathbf{b}^2 - 4\mathbf{a}\mathbf{c}). \tag{2.54}$$

We now take the square root of the vectors on both sides of

Eq. (2.54) by the method described in Section 1.5, thereby obtaining

$$\mathbf{as} + \tfrac{1}{2}\mathbf{b} = \pm\tfrac{1}{2}(\mathbf{b}^2 - 4\mathbf{ac})^{1/2} \tag{2.55}$$

or

$$\mathbf{as} = -\tfrac{1}{2}\mathbf{b} \pm \tfrac{1}{2}(\mathbf{b}^2 - 4\mathbf{ac})^{1/2}. \tag{2.56}$$

Finally we take the quotient of the vectors on both sides of Eq. (2.56) by the vector **a**, thereby obtaining

$$\mathbf{s} = \frac{-\mathbf{b} \pm (\mathbf{b}^2 - 4\mathbf{ac})^{1/2}}{2\mathbf{a}}. \tag{2.57}$$

We thus see that there are two vectors **s** that make the vector on the left-hand side of Eq. (2.51) vanish. One is the vector

$$\mathbf{s}_1 = \frac{-\mathbf{b} + (\mathbf{b}^2 - 4\mathbf{ac})^{1/2}}{2\mathbf{a}} \tag{2.58}$$

and the other is the vector

$$\mathbf{s}_2 = \frac{-\mathbf{b} - (\mathbf{b}^2 - 4\mathbf{ac})^{1/2}}{2\mathbf{a}}. \tag{2.59}$$

It is important to notice that the products $\mathbf{b}^2$ and **ac** under the radical sign in Eqs. (2.58) and (2.59) are planar products of vectors. It is also important to notice that the radical in Eqs. (2.58) and (2.59) involves the square root of a vector $\mathbf{b}^2 - 4\mathbf{ac}$ calculated by the method described in Section 1.5. Finally, it is important to notice that division by **a** in Eqs. (2.58) and (2.59) involves the quotient of two vectors, to be calculated by the method described in Section 1.3.

In terms of the vectors $\mathbf{s}_1$ and $\mathbf{s}_2$ defined by Eqs. (2.58) and (2.59), the expression on the left-hand side of Eq. (2.51) may be written in the factorized form

$$\mathbf{a}(\mathbf{s} - \mathbf{s}_1)(\mathbf{s} - \mathbf{s}_2). \tag{2.60}$$

If we multiply out expression (2.60), its identity with the left-hand side of Eq. (2.51) implies that

$$\mathbf{s}_1 + \mathbf{s}_2 = -\mathbf{b}/\mathbf{a} \tag{2.61}$$

and

$$\mathbf{s}_1\mathbf{s}_2 = \mathbf{c}/\mathbf{a}. \tag{2.62}$$

These equations may also be verified from Eqs. (2.58) and (2.59). Equation (2.61) states that the vector sum of the roots of the quadratic equation (2.51) is equal in magnitude and opposite in direction to the quotient of the vector coefficient **b** by the vector coefficient **a**. Equation (2.62) states that the planar product of the roots of the quadratic equation (2.51) is equal to the quotient of the vector coefficient **c** by the vector coefficient **a**.

Let us illustrate the solution of the vector quadratic equation (2.51) for the circumstances when

$$\mathbf{a} = 1 \angle 0 \tag{2.63}$$

$$\mathbf{b} = 2 \angle \frac{\pi}{6} \tag{2.64}$$

$$\mathbf{c} = \sqrt{3} \angle \frac{\pi}{6}. \tag{2.65}$$

To evaluate the radical in Eq. (2.57) we first evaluate the vectors $\mathbf{b}^2$ and $4\mathbf{ac}$. Application of the planar product rule to Eq. (2.64) gives

$$\mathbf{b}^2 = 4 \angle \frac{\pi}{3} = 2 + \mathbf{j}\, 2\sqrt{3}. \tag{2.66}$$

Application of the planar product rule to Eqs. (2.63) and (2.65) gives

$$4\mathbf{ac} = 4\sqrt{3} \angle \frac{\pi}{6} = 6 + \mathbf{j}\, 2\sqrt{3}. \tag{2.67}$$

Vector substraction of Eq. (2.67) from Eq. (2.66) then gives

$$\mathbf{b}^2 - 4\mathbf{ac} = -4 + \mathbf{j}0 = 4 \angle \pm\pi. \tag{2.68}$$

The vectors corresponding to Eqs. (2.66), (2.67), and (2.68) are illustrated in Fig. 2.9. We now take the square root of the vector given in Eq. (2.68) by the method described in Section 1.5. We obtain

$$\pm(\mathbf{b}^2 - 4\mathbf{ac})^{1/2} = 2 \angle \pm\tfrac{1}{2}\pi. \tag{2.69}$$

Since **a** is a unit vector in the reference direction, Eqs. (2.57) may be written

$$\mathbf{s} = -\tfrac{1}{2}\mathbf{b} \pm \tfrac{1}{2}(\mathbf{b}^2 - 4\mathbf{ac})^{1/2}. \tag{2.70}$$

The two vectors involved on the right-hand side of this equation may now be derived from Eqs. (2.64) and (2.69). The way in which these vectors are combined in accordance with Eq. (2.70)

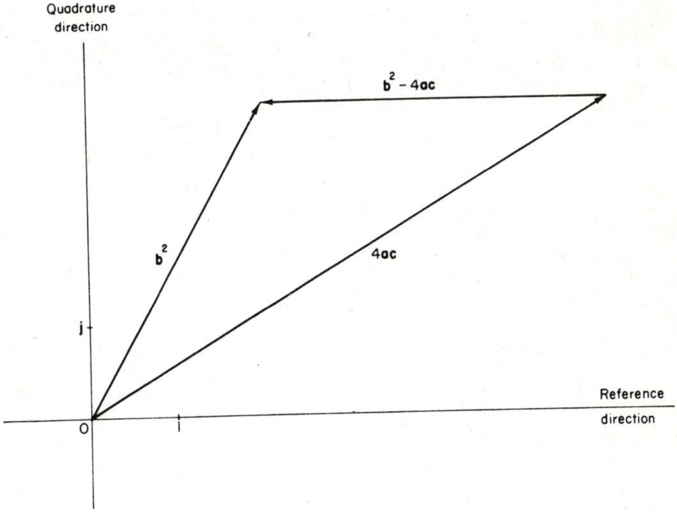

FIG. 2.9. Illustrating calculation of the vector under the radical sign in Eq. (2.57).

is illustrated in Fig. 2.10. From the geometry of Fig. 2.10 we see that the two vector solutions of the vector algebraic equation (2.51) when the vector coefficients are given by Eqs. (2.63), (2.64), and (2.65) are

$$\mathbf{s}_1 = 1 \angle \frac{5\pi}{6} \tag{2.71}$$

and

$$\mathbf{s}_2 = \sqrt{3} \angle -\frac{2\pi}{3}. \tag{2.72}$$

Let us now verify the validity of the roots given by Eqs. (2.71) and (2.72). Figure 2.11 illustrates the verification of the solution given by Eq. (2.71), and Fig. 2.12 that given by Eq. (2.72). In

Fig. 2.11(b) is illustrated the vector **c** given by Eq. (2.65). There is also illustrated the vector $\mathbf{bs}_1$ calculated by the planar product rule from Eqs. (2.64) and (2.71). Finally there is illustrated in Fig. 2.11(b) the vector $\mathbf{as}_1{}^2$ calculated by the planar product rule from Eqs. (2.63) and (2.71). These three vectors are, respectively, the third, second, and first terms of the expression on the left-hand side of Eq. (2.51). The fact that these three vectors sum to a zero resultant in Fig. 2.11(b) verifies that the vector $\mathbf{s}_1$ given

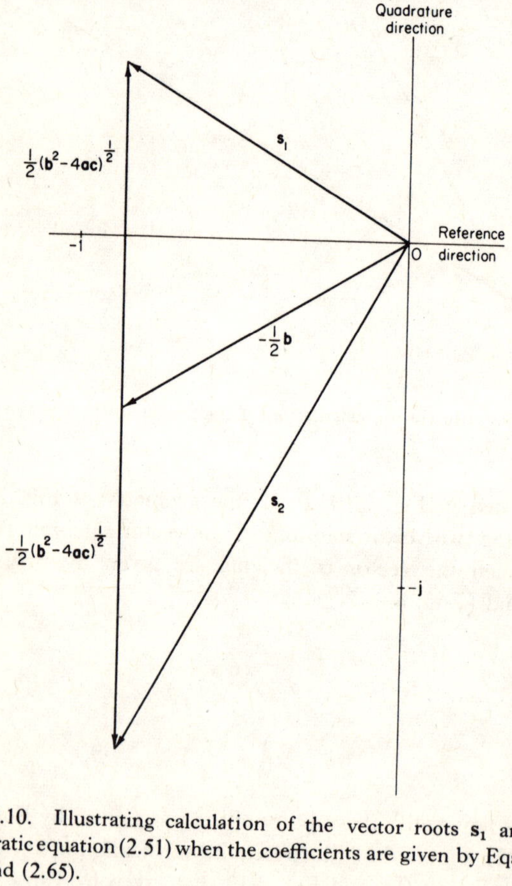

FIG. 2.10. Illustrating calculation of the vector roots $\mathbf{s}_1$ and $\mathbf{s}_2$ of the quadratic equation (2.51) when the coefficients are given by Eqs. (2.63), (2.64), and (2.65).

by Eq. (2.71) is a root of the quadratic equation. Figure 2.12 presents the same calculation for the vector root $\mathbf{s}_2$ given by Eq. (2.72).

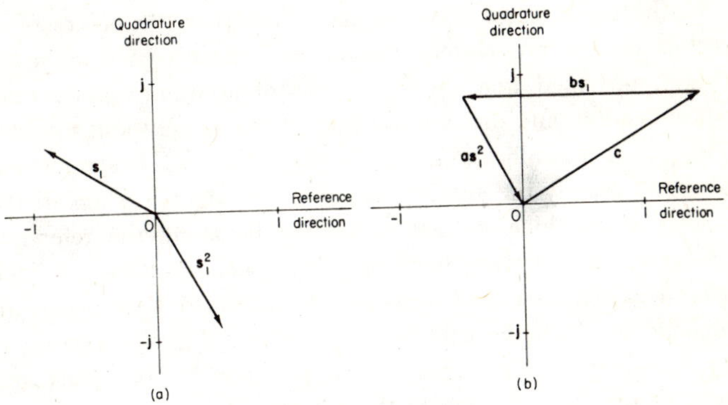

FIG. 2.11. Illustrating verification of the root in Eq. (2.71) of the quadratic equation (2.51) when the coefficients are given by Eqs. (2.63), (2.64), and (2.65).

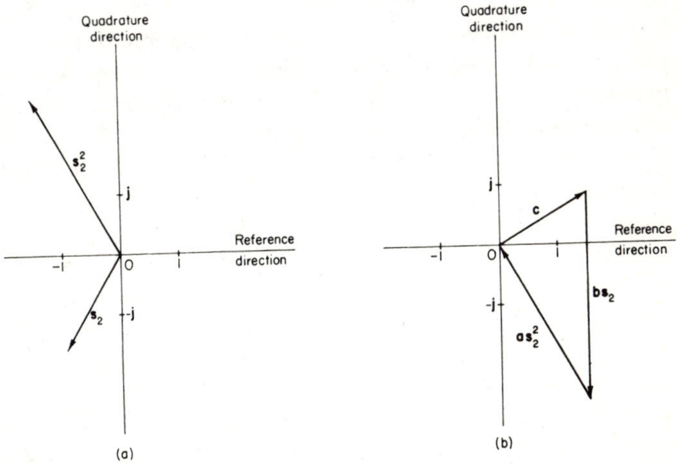

FIG. 2.12. Illlustrating verification of the root in Eq. (2.72) of the quadratic equation (2.51) when the coefficients are given by Eqs. (2.63), (2.64), and (2.65).

2.5. Relation between Vector Algebra and Scalar Algebra

In the preceding section we have seen that the processes of vector algebra are closely related to the processes of scalar algebra provided that the operations of addition, subtraction, multiplication, and division are interpreted as addition, subtraction, planar multiplication, and division of vectors. Scalar algebra is in fact merely the special case of vector algebra when all the vectors with which we are concerned lie along the reference axis. Positive numbers correspond to vectors drawn in the reference direction and negative numbers to vectors drawn opposite to the reference direction. Thus, if scalar algebra is carried out in vector language, a positive number is represented by a vector at zero angle to the reference direction, whereas a negative number is represented as a vector at angle π with the reference direction. The planar product of two vectors both at a zero angle with the reference direction is another vector at zero angle with the reference direction. This is the vector equivalent of the statement in scalar algebra that the product of two positive numbers is a positive number. The planar product of two vectors at angle π with the reference direction is a vector at angle 2π with the reference direction, and this is a vector in the reference direction. This is the vector equivalent of the statement in scalar algebra that the product of two negative numbers is a positive number. The planar product of a vector at angle zero with the reference direction and a vector at angle π with the reference direction is another vector at angle π with the reference direction. This is the vector equivalent of the statement in scalar algebra that the product of a positive number and a negative number is a negative number. Thus, the whole of scalar algebra may be carried out in the language of vector algebra if positive numbers are represented by vectors in the reference direction and negative numbers are represented by vectors in the opposite direction.

As an example, let us suppose that we are to discuss in scalar algebra the quadratic function of a scalar quantity s represented by

$$P(s) = 3 + 4s + s^2. \tag{2.73}$$

If

$$s = 2 \tag{2.74}$$

we deduce from Eq. (2.73) that

$$P = 15. \tag{2.75}$$

If on the other hand

$$s = -2 \tag{2.76}$$

we deduce from Eq. (2.73) that

$$P = -1. \tag{2.77}$$

Let us consider how these statements would be made in vector algebra. In vector algebra we consider the polynomial function of the vector **s** given by

$$\mathbf{P}(\mathbf{s}) = 3 + 4\mathbf{s} + \mathbf{s}^2. \tag{2.78}$$

In accordance with our contracted notation, it is understood that the first term on the right-hand side of Eq. (2.78) is the coefficient of a unit vector in the reference direction. By the method described in connection with Fig. 2.8 the magnitude and direction of the vector **P** defined by Eq. (2.78) may be calculated for any given magnitude and direction of **s**. Corresponding to the positive value 2 for s in Eq. (2.74), let us consider a vector of magnitude 2 in the reference direction, so that

$$\mathbf{s} = 2 \angle 0. \tag{2.79}$$

If, for Eqs. (2.78) and (2.79), we draw a vector diagram of the type shown in Fig. 2.8, we obtain the diagram shown in Fig. 2.13. The vectors in Fig. 2.13(b) have been drawn slightly above or below the reference axis to permit verification of the vector addition. We see from Fig. 2.13(b) that, corresponding to the vector **s** given by Eq. (2.79), the vector **P** in Eq. (2.78) evaluates to

$$\mathbf{P} = 15 \angle 0. \tag{2.80}$$

Equations (2.79) and (2.80) merely state in vector language the information conveyed in scalar language by Eqs. (2.74) and (2.75).

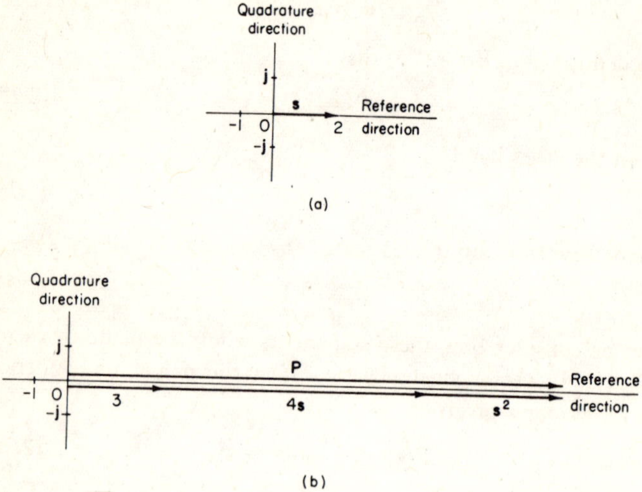

FIG. 2.13. Illustrating (a) the vector **s** given by Eq. (2.79), and (b) calculation of the corresponding vector **P** given by Eq. (2.78).

Corresponding to the negative value —2 for s in Eq. (2.76), let us now consider a vector of magnitude 2 in the direction opposite to the reference direction, so that

$$\mathbf{s} = 2 \angle \pi. \tag{2.81}$$

This situation is illustrated in Fig. 2.14, and we see that

$$\mathbf{P} = 1 \angle \pi. \tag{2.82}$$

Equations (2.81) and (2.82) are the vector equivalents of the statements in scalar algebra represented by Eqs. (2.76) and (2.77).

That scalar algebra is merely the particular case of vector algebra when all the vectors concerned lie along the reference axis may also be illustrated with the aid of quadratic equations.

In scalar algebra a quadratic equation for a scalar quantity s is written

$$as^2 + bs + c = 0 \tag{2.83}$$

where a, b, and c are scalar quantities that are positive, negative, or zero. As is well known, the solution of the scalar quadratic equation (2.83) is

$$s = \frac{-b \pm (b^2 - 4ac)^{1/2}}{2a}. \tag{2.84}$$

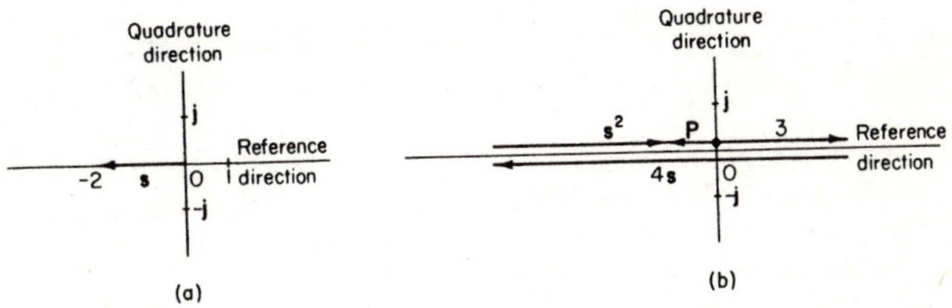

FIG. 2.14. Illustrating (a) the vector **s** given by Eqs. (2.81), and (b) calculation of the corresponding vector **P** in accordance with Eq. (2.78).

A simple example is provided by the quadratic equation

$$s^2 + 4s + 3 = 0 \tag{2.85}$$

for which the roots are

$$s_1 = -1 \tag{2.86}$$

and

$$s_2 = -3. \tag{2.87}$$

The scalar quadratic equation (2.85) may be rewritten in the vector form shown in Eq. (2.51) if

$$\begin{aligned} \mathbf{a} &= 1 \angle 0 \\ \mathbf{b} &= 4 \angle 0 \\ \mathbf{c} &= 3 \angle 0. \end{aligned} \tag{2.88}$$

In these circumstances Figs. 2.9 and 2.10 take the form shown in Figs. 2.15 and 2.16, and the roots are

$$\mathbf{s}_1 = 1 \angle \pi \tag{2.89}$$

$$\mathbf{s}_2 = 3 \angle \pi. \tag{2.90}$$

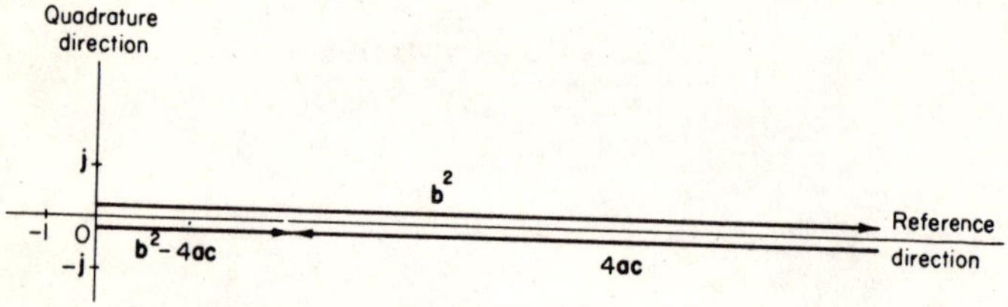

FIG. 2.15. Illustrating calculation of the vector under the radical sign in Eqs. (2.57) for the conditions specified in Eqs. (2.88).

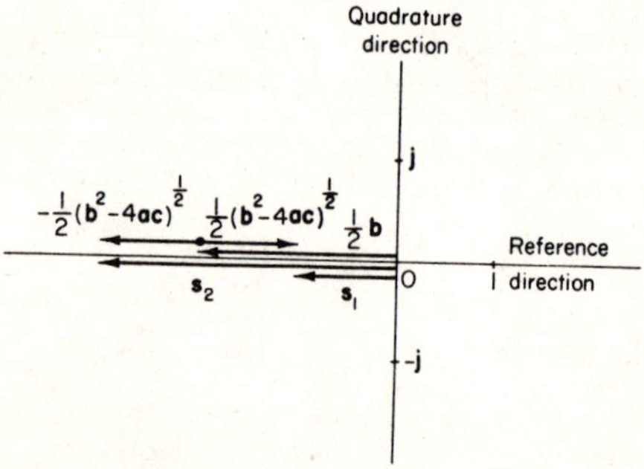

FIG. 2.16. Illustrating calculation of the roots of Eq. (2.51) for the conditions specified in Eqs. (2.88).

Equations (2.89) and (2.90) restate in vector language the information conveyed in scalar language by Eqs. (2.86) and (2.87). The verification of the solutions given in Eqs. (2.89) and (2.90) are illustrated in Figs. 2.17 and 2.18. Figures 2.17 and 2.18 are what Figs. 2.11 and 2.12 become when the vector coefficients in Eq. (2.51) are given by Eqs. (2.88).

It is important to notice that, if we restrict ourselves to scalar algebra, the quadratic equation (2.83) has solutions given by Eqs. (2.84) only if

$$b^2 \geqslant 4ac. \tag{2.91}$$

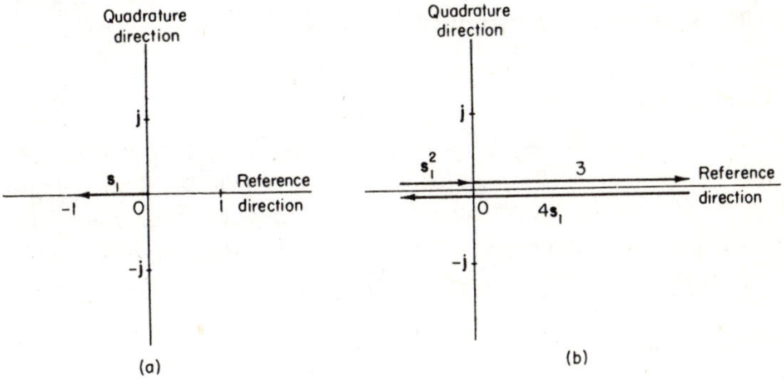

FIG. 2.17. Illustrating calculation of the expression on the left-hand side of Eq. (2.51) for the conditions specified in Eqs. (2.88) and (2.89).

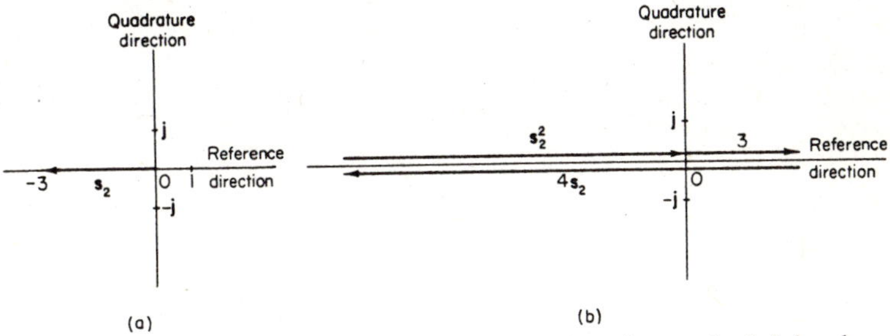

FIG. 2.18. Illustrating calculation of the expression on the left-hand side of Eq. (2.51) for the conditions specified in Eqs. (2.88) and (2.90).

If, on the other hand,

$$b^2 < 4ac \tag{2.92}$$

then the number under the radical sign in Eq. (2.84) is negative. There is no arithmetical square root of a negative number, and consequently Eq. (2.83) has no solution in scalar algebra under the conditions of inequality (2.92). In vector algebra, however, a quadratic equation always has two solutions given by Eqs. (2.57). In vector algebra the quantity under the radical sign in Eqs. (2.57) is a vector; and its square root is taken as shown in Fig. 1.8. If the vector under the radical sign in Eq. (2.57) happens to point in the direction opposite to the reference direction, then its square root is taken as shown in Fig. 1.9(b). As an example let us consider the scalar quadratic equation

$$s^2 + 2s + 5 = 0. \tag{2.93}$$

This equation satisfied the inequality (2.92). Consequently there is no scalar quantity s for which the expression on the left-hand side of Eq. (2.93) vanishes. This is illustrated in Fig. 2.19, which shows the graph of this function of s. On the other hand, if we consider the vector equation

$$\mathbf{s}^2 + 2\mathbf{s} + 5 = 0 \tag{2.94}$$

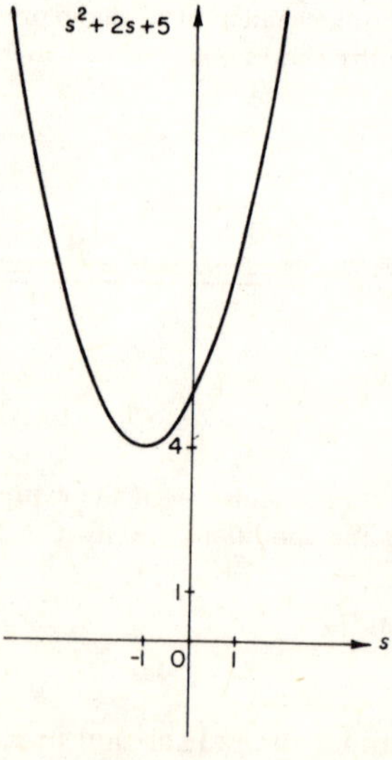

FIG. 2.19. Illustrating the fact that the quadratic equation (2.93) has no scalar root.

then the vector on the left-hand side vanishes for a pair of vectors **s** neither of which lie along the reference axis. Equation (2.94) is identical with Eq. (2.51) if

$$\mathbf{a} = 1 \angle 0$$
$$\mathbf{b} = 2 \angle 0 \qquad (2.95)$$
$$\mathbf{c} = 5 \angle 0.$$

With these expressions for the vectors **a**, **b**, and **c**, Fig. 2.9 takes the form shown in Fig. 2.20. We see that the vector $\mathbf{b}^2 - 4\mathbf{ac}$

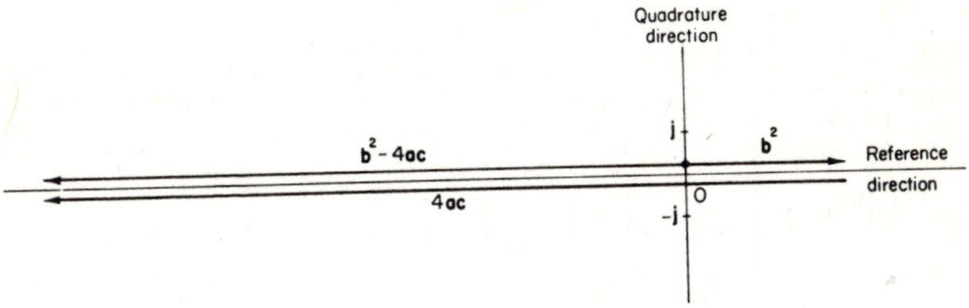

FIG. 2.20. Illustrating calculation of the vector under the radical sign in Eqs. (2.57) under the conditions specified in Eqs. (2.95).

points in the negative reference direction, so that its square root must be taken as shown in Fig. 1.9(b). As a result, Fig. 2.10 takes the form shown in Fig. 2.21. The two solutions of the quadratic equation evaluate to

$$\mathbf{s}_1 = -1 + \mathbf{j}2 \qquad (2.96)$$

$$\mathbf{s}_2 = -1 - \mathbf{j}2. \qquad (2.97)$$

Thus, while there is no scalar quantity *s* that satisfies the scalar quadratic equation (2.93), there are a pair of vectors given by Eqs. (2.96) and (2.97) that satisfy the vector quadratic equation (2.94), but neither of these vectors lie along the reference axis. The roots given in Eqs. (2.96) and (2.97) of the quadratic equation (2.94) may be verified as shown in Figs. 2.22 and 2.23, which are what Figs. 2.11 and 2.12 become when the coefficients of the quadratic equation (2.51) are given by Eqs. (2.95).

Great practical importance attaches to quadratic equations with scalar coefficients for which inequality (2.92) is satisfied. Figures 2.20 through 2.23 demonstrate the fact that such equations can be solved only in terms of vectors and that the two vector solutions are mirror images of each other in the reference axis. Such roots of an algebraic equation with scalar

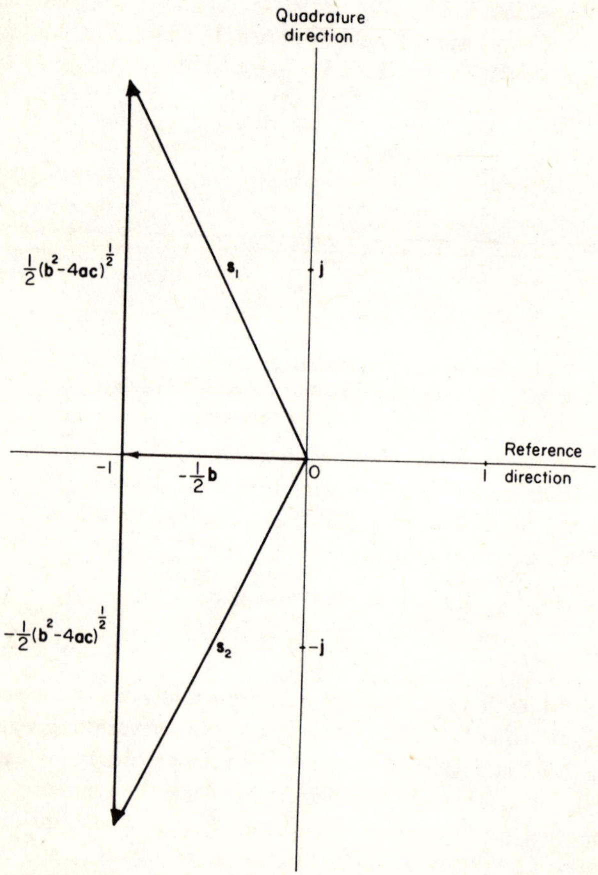

FIG. 2.21. Illustrating calculation of the roots of the quadratic equation (2.51) under the conditions specified in Eqs. (2.95).

coefficients are what mathematicians call "conjugate complex roots."

The upshot of our investigation in this chapter of vector algebra using planar products and quotients is that the methods

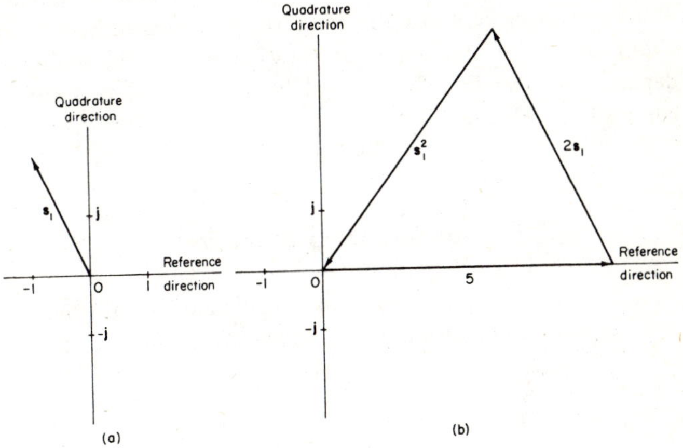

FIG. 2.22. Illustrating verification of the solution of the quadratic equation (2.94) given by Eq. (2.96).

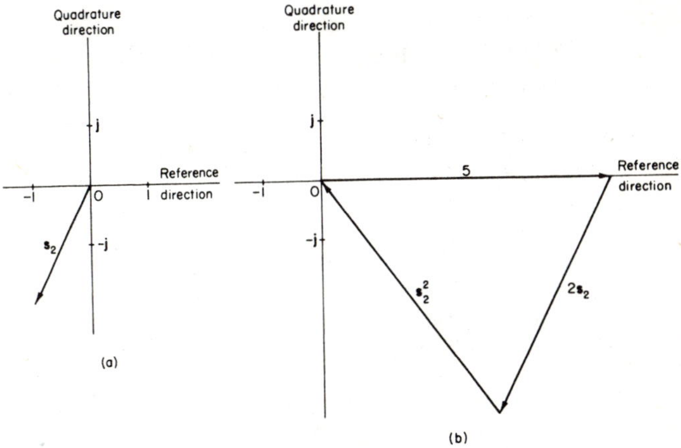

FIG. 2.23. Illustrating verification of the solution of the quadratic equation (2.94) given by Eq. (2.97).

of scalar algebra are directly adaptable to vector algebra. In all cases the vector character of the algebraic expression must be carefully and completely interpreted, and this is usually best done with the aid of vector diagrams. In this way polynominal functions of a vector may be factorized, and algebraic functions of a vector may be written in the form discussed in Section 2.2. From the poles and zeros of these functions the functional dependence may then be derived by the method described in connection with Fig. 2.4.

Summarizing Exercises

2.1. Explain what is meant by a polynomial function of a vector **s**. Illustrate the evaluation of such a function graphically.

2.2. Explain the vector significance of the quadratic equation

$$\mathbf{a}\mathbf{s}^2 + \mathbf{b}\mathbf{s} + \mathbf{c} = 0$$

for **s** and derive its solutions.

2.3. In the previous exercise show that the vector sum of the two solutions is $-\mathbf{b}/\mathbf{a}$ and the planar product of the two solutions is $\mathbf{c}/\mathbf{a}$.

2.4. Solve the quadratic equation in Exercise 2.2 if $\mathbf{a} = 1 \angle 0$, $\mathbf{b} = 2 \angle \frac{1}{6}\pi$, and $\mathbf{c} = \sqrt{3} \angle \frac{1}{6}\pi$. Illustrate the process of solution by means of vector diagrams. Draw vector diagrams to verify the validity of the solutions.

2.5. Explain why vector algebra using planar products and quotients reduces to scalar algebra when all the vectors involved lie along the reference axis.

2.6. Solve the quadratic equation in Exercice 2.2 if $\mathbf{a} = 1 \angle 0$, $\mathbf{b} = 4 \angle 0$, and $\mathbf{c} = 3 \angle 0$ (a) by factorization and (b) by substitution into the solutions derived in Exercise 2.2. Illustrate the latter process of solution by means of vector diagrams. Draw vector diagrams to verify the validity of the solutions. Explain the relation to scalar algebra.

2.7. If a, b, and c are scalar quantities, show that the quadratic equation

$$as^2 + bs + c = 0$$

for s has scalar solutions if and only if $b^2 \geqslant 4ac$. Explain why the quadratic equation has vector solutions if $b^2 < 4ac$. Show that the vector solutions are mirror images of each other in the reference axis.

2.8. Solve the quadratic equation in Exercise 2.2 if $\mathbf{a} = 1 \angle 0$, $\mathbf{b} = 2 \angle 0$, and $\mathbf{c} = 5 \angle 0$. Illustrate the process of solution by means of vector diagrams. Draw vector diagrams to verify the validity of the solutions.

2.9. Explain what are meant by the poles and zeros of the algebraic function of $\mathbf{s}$ specified by

$$\mathbf{F}(\mathbf{s}) = \frac{(\mathbf{s} - \mathbf{s}_1')(\mathbf{s} - \mathbf{s}_2') \cdots (\mathbf{s} - \mathbf{s}_m')}{(\mathbf{s} - \mathbf{s}_1)(\mathbf{s} - \mathbf{s}_2) \cdots (\mathbf{s} - \mathbf{s}_n)} .$$

Describe a method for evaluating the vector $\mathbf{F}$ in magnitude and direction when the vectors $\mathbf{s}$, $\mathbf{s}_1$, $\mathbf{s}_2$, ..., $\mathbf{s}_n$, $\mathbf{s}_1'$, ..., $\mathbf{s}_m'$ are specified in magnitude and direction.

2.10. Evaluate the vector

$$\frac{(\mathbf{s} - \mathbf{s}_1')(\mathbf{s} - \mathbf{s}_2')}{(\mathbf{s} - \mathbf{s}_1)(\mathbf{s} - \mathbf{s}_2)}$$

when $\mathbf{s} = 2\mathbf{j}$, $\mathbf{s}_1 = -2 + \mathbf{j}$, $\mathbf{s}_2 = -2 - \mathbf{j}$, $\mathbf{s}_1' = -1 + 2\mathbf{j}$, and $\mathbf{s}_2' = -1 - 2\mathbf{j}$. Illustrate the evaluation by means of a vector diagram.

CHAPTER 3

GRAPHICAL REPRESENTATION OF VECTOR FUNCTIONS OF A VECTOR

3.1. Introduction

In the previous chapter we investigated vector-algebraic functions of a vector of the form

$$\mathbf{F}(\mathbf{s}) = \frac{(\mathbf{s} - \mathbf{s}_1')(\mathbf{s} - \mathbf{s}_2') \cdots (\mathbf{s} - \mathbf{s}_m')}{(\mathbf{s} - \mathbf{s}_1)(\mathbf{s} - \mathbf{s}_2) \cdots (\mathbf{s} - \mathbf{s}_n)} . \tag{3.1}$$

Here $\mathbf{s}_1, \mathbf{s}_2, \ldots \mathbf{s}_n ; \mathbf{s}_1', \mathbf{s}_2', \ldots \mathbf{s}_m'$ are fixed vectors, and $\mathbf{s}$ is a vector that can vary in magnitude and direction. By the methods developed in Chapter 2 we know how to derive the functional dependence of the vector $\mathbf{F}$ on the vector $\mathbf{s}$. We now have to consider how this functional dependence can be conveniently represented graphically.

For a scalar function of a scalar variable, graphical representation is conveniently achieved by using Cartesian coordinates to draw a curve showing the variation of the dependent variable with the independent variable. However, for a vector function $\mathbf{F}(\mathbf{s})$ of a vector variable $\mathbf{s}$, both the independent variable $\mathbf{s}$ and the dependent variable $\mathbf{F}$ are vectors that have to be represented both in magnitude and direction. Thus, $|\mathbf{F}|$ has to be represented as a function of both the magnitude and direction of **s**, while $\angle$**F** also has to be represented as a function of both the magnitude and direction of **s**. These graphical representations are conveniently achieved with the aid of contour maps.

To draw contour maps for a given function **F**(**s**) we proceed as follows: In the plane of the paper we choose an origin *O* and a reference direction. In this plane the independent variable **s** is represented as a position vector, and the plane is known as the **s** plane. At the tip of the position vector **s** in the **s** plane we now mark the numerical values of | **F** | and $\angle$**F**. Let us imagine that this has been done for a large number of position vectors **s** in the **s** plane. We may now draw a contour line through points having the same value of | **F** |, and mark the contour line with the value of | **F** | concerned. A large number of such contour lines may be marked on the map, preferably at equal intervals of | **F** |. We then have the required contour map for | **F** |. The contour map is conveniently regarded as representing a terrain, the height of which is the magnitude of | **F** |. In the same way, from the calculations of $\angle$**F** we may draw a contour map in which the contour lines are marked according to the values of $\angle$**F**.

For a given function **F**(**s**), the two contour maps for | **F** | and $\angle$**F** are conveniently drawn on the same **s** plane. We may then use the resulting map of the function **F**(**s**) as follows: Through the tip of the position vector **s**, there run two contour lines. One of these lines is marked with a value of | **F** | and the other with a value of $\angle$**F**. These two values give the magnitude and angle of the vector **F** corresponding to the chosen position vector **s**. Let us apply this method of graphical representation to some simple vector functions of **s**.

3.2. Contour Map for a Function Involving a Simple Zero

Let us consider the function in Eq. (3.1) when there is one factor in the numerator and none in the denominator. We then have the function

$$\mathbf{F}(\mathbf{s}) = \mathbf{s} - \mathbf{s}_0 \tag{3.2}$$

where $\mathbf{s}_0$ is a fixed vector and $\mathbf{s}$ is a variable vector. In the $\mathbf{s}$ plane the magnitude of the vector $\mathbf{F}$ given by Eq. (3.2) vanishes at the point whose position vector is $\mathbf{s}_0$. We are thus dealing with a function that has a zero at the position $\mathbf{s}_0$ in the $\mathbf{s}$ plane.

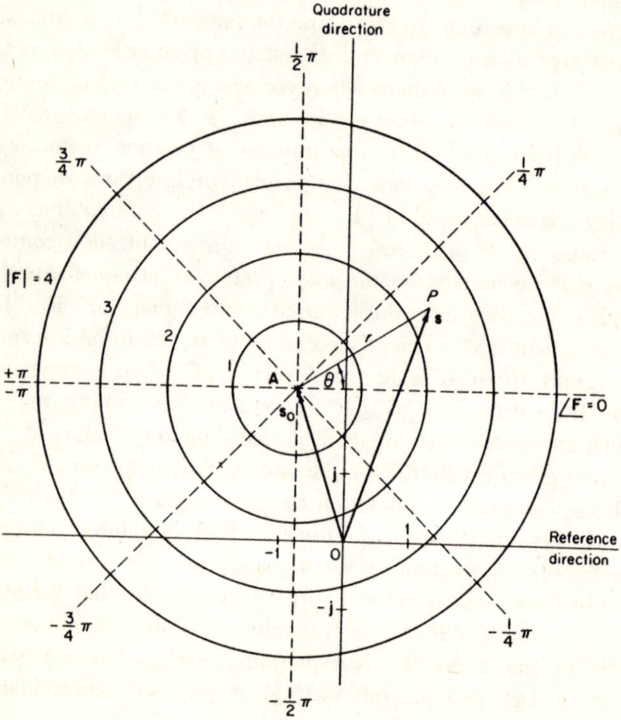

FIG. 3.1. Contour map for the function $\mathbf{F}(\mathbf{s}) = \mathbf{s} - \mathbf{s}_0$.

The contour map for the function in Eq. (3.2) is shown in Fig. 3.1. The circles concentric with the points $\mathbf{s}_0$ are the magnitude contours, marked in equal intervals of $|\mathbf{F}|$. The broken straight lines radiating from the points $\mathbf{s}_0$ are the angle contours, marked in equal intervals of $\angle\mathbf{F}$. One of these lines has the double marking $\pm\pi$; however the vector $\mathbf{F}$ is in the same direction whether it makes with the reference direction a counterclockwise angle $+\pi$ or a counterclockwise angle $-\pi$. The vector $\overrightarrow{OA}$ is $\mathbf{s}_0$ so that the point A is the zero of the function. The vector $\overrightarrow{OP}$ represents a typical position vector $\mathbf{s}$. Through P there is a magnitude contour and an angle contour; the markings on these contours give the magnitude and counterclockwise angle of the vector $\mathbf{F}$ given by Eq. (3.2) when $\mathbf{s}$ has its tip at the point P.

The vector $\overrightarrow{AP}$ in Fig. 3.1 is the vector difference between $\mathbf{s}$ and $\mathbf{s}_0$, and is consequently the vector on the right-hand side of Eq. (3.2). If the vector $\overrightarrow{AP}$ has magnitude r and makes a counterclockwise angle θ with the reference direction, we may write

$$\mathbf{s} - \mathbf{s}_0 = r \angle\theta. \tag{3.3}$$

Substitution from Eq. (3.3) into Eq. (3.2) then gives

$$\mathbf{F} = r \angle\theta \tag{3.4}$$

so that

$$|\mathbf{F}| = r \tag{3.5}$$

and

$$\angle\mathbf{F} = \theta. \tag{3.6}$$

Equation (3.5) shows that the contour lines $|\mathbf{F}| =$ constant are the circles $r =$ constant with centers at the point A in Fig. 3.1. The contour marking on a particular circle is simply equal to the radius of the circle. Equation (3.6) shows that the contour lines $\angle\mathbf{F} =$ constant are the radial lines $\theta =$ constant drawn from the point A in Fig. 3.1. Moreover the contour marking on a particular line is simply equal to the counterclockwise angle that this line makes with the reference direction.

The terrain represented by the magnitude contours in Fig. 3.1 has zero height at the point A and rises uniformly as we move away from A in any direction. In accordance with Eq. (3.5) the height of the terrain is equal to the horizontal distance from A, so that the terrain slopes upwards from the point A at 45° in all directions. On this terrain the angle contours in

Fig. 3.1 are the lines of steepest ascent or descent, and this is the most convenient way of picturing the angle contours. The function whose contour map is shown in Fig. 3.1 is the simplest function having a zero at the point *A*. The terrain behavior shown in Fig. 3.1 is typical of the behavior in the neighborhood of a simple zero of any function.

The particular case of the contour map shown in Fig. 3.1 that occurs when the vector $\mathbf{s}_0$ vanishes is shown in Fig. 3.2. From Eq. (3.2), the function whose contour map is shown in Fig. 3.2 is therefore

$$\mathbf{F}(\mathbf{s}) = \mathbf{s}. \tag{3.7}$$

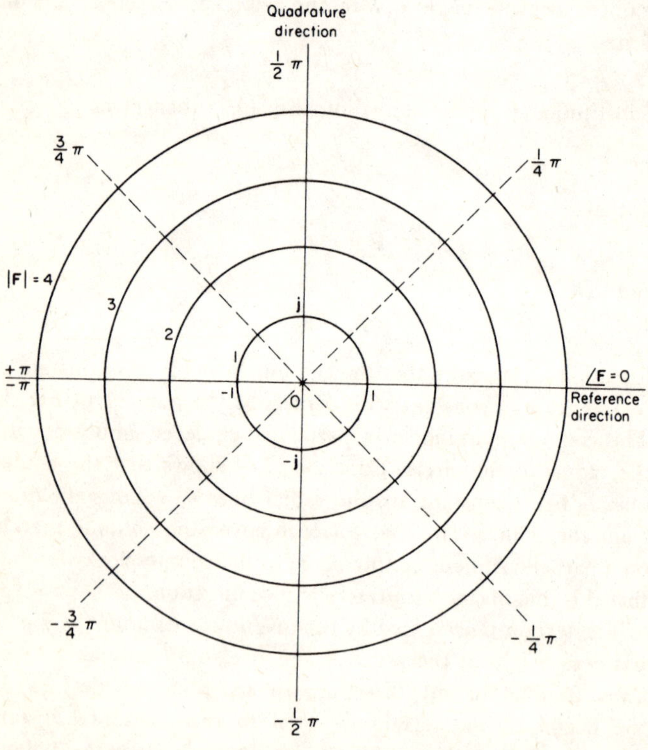

FIG. 3.2. Contour map for the function $\mathbf{F}(\mathbf{s}) = \mathbf{s}$.

This is the simplest function having a zero at the origin in the **s** plane. The contour map shown in Fig. 3.1 is obtained by giving a vector displacement $\mathbf{s}_0$ to the contour map shown in Fig. 3.2.

3.3. Contour Map for a Function Involving a Simple Pole

Let us now examine a contour map for a function of **s** of the type appearing in Eq. (3.1) when there is one factor in the denominator and none in the numerator. In these circumstances we are considering the function

$$\mathbf{F}(\mathbf{s}) = \frac{1}{\mathbf{s} - \mathbf{s}_0} \tag{3.8}$$

where $\mathbf{s}_0$ is a fixed vector and **s** is a vector that is variable in magnitude and direction. This is a function that possesses a pole at the point whose position vector in the **s** plane is $\mathbf{s}_0$.

The contour map in the **s** plane for the function appearing in Eq. (3.8) is shown in Fig. 3.3. The vector $\overrightarrow{OA}$ is the vector $\mathbf{s}_0$, so that A is a pole of the function. The vector $\overrightarrow{OP}$ represents an arbitrary position vector **s**, so that the vector $\overrightarrow{AP}$ is the one appearing in Eq. (3.3). On the right-hand side of Eq. (3.8) we have the reciprocal of the vector in Eq. (3.3). Interpreting the numerator on the right-hand side of Eq. (3.8) as a unit vector in the reference direction, we see that evaluation of **F**(**s**) involves forming the quotient of the vector $1 \angle 0$ by the vector $r \angle \theta$. In accordance with the quotient rule we therefore obtain

$$\mathbf{F}(\mathbf{s}) = \frac{1}{r} \angle -\theta \tag{3.9}$$

from which it follows

$$|\mathbf{F}| = \frac{1}{r} \tag{3.10}$$

and

$$\angle \mathbf{F} = -\theta \tag{3.11}$$

From Eq. (3.10) we see that the magnitude contours $|\mathbf{F}| =$ constant are the circles $r =$ constant shown in Fig. 3.3, and the marking on a particular contour is equal to the reciprocal of the radius of the circle. Likewise, it follows from Eq. (3.11) that the angle contours $\angle\mathbf{F} =$ constant are the radial lines $\theta =$ constant drawn from the point A in Fig. 3.3. Notice that, in accordance

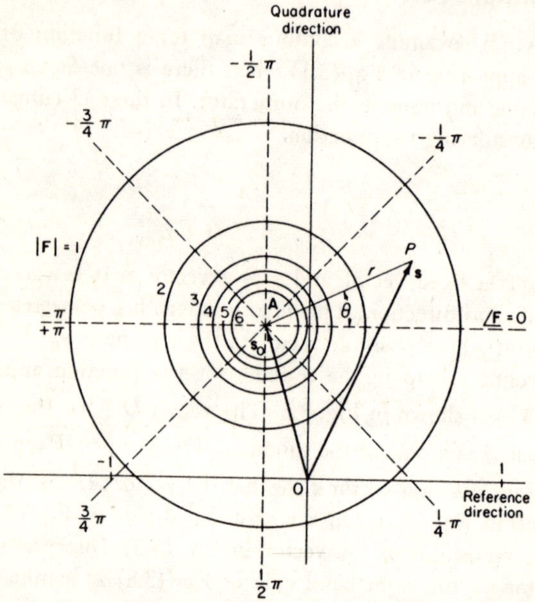

FIG. 3.3. Contour map for the function $\mathbf{F}(\mathbf{s}) = 1/(\mathbf{s} - \mathbf{s}_0)$.

with the negative sign in Eq. (3.11), the markings on the angle contours decrease as we move round the point A in the counter-clockwise direction. Through the point P in Fig. 3.3 there pass a magnitude contour and an angle contour, and the markings on these contours give the magnitude and angle of the vector $\mathbf{F}$ in Eq. (3.8) when the position vector $\mathbf{s}$ is $\overrightarrow{OP}$.

The terrain represented by the magnitude contours in Fig. 3.3 consists of an indefinitely high peak at the point A. The terrain slopes away from the point A, steeply at first and then more gradually, the height ultimately tending to zero at an indefinitely large distance from A. The angle contours are again most conveniently regarded as the lines of steepest ascent and descent on the terrain represented by the magnitude contours.

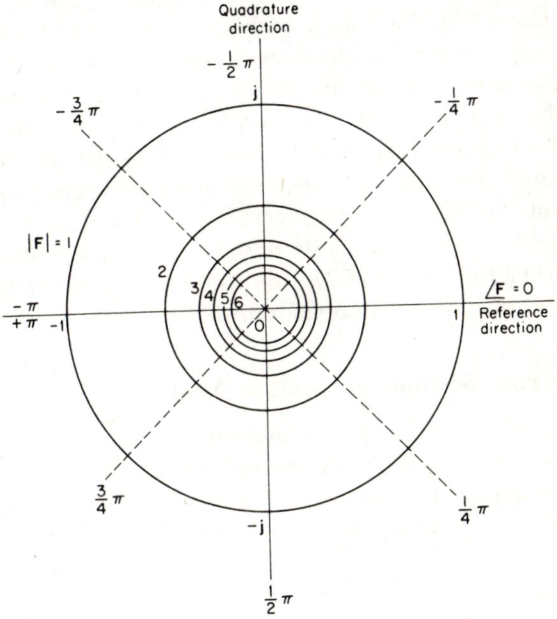

FIG. 3.4. Contour map for the function $\mathbf{F(s)} = 1/\mathbf{s}$.

Figure 3.4 shows what the contour map in Fig. 3.3 becomes when $\mathbf{s}_0$ vanishes. The function whose contour map is shown in Fig. 3.4 is therefore

$$\mathbf{F(s)} = \frac{1}{\mathbf{s}} \cdot \tag{3.12}$$

Figure 3.4 illustrates the contour map for the simplest function having a simple pole at the origin. The contour map in Fig. 3.3

is obtained by giving a vector displacement $\mathbf{s}_0$ to the contour map in Fig. 3.4.

Figures 3.1 through 3.4 illustrate quite simple but quite important examples of contour maps representing vector functions of a vector. Many such contour maps are encountered in practice. A substantial collection of interesting contour maps is to be found in "Tables of Higher Functions" by Jahnke, Emde, and Lösch.* It is a general feature of these contour maps that the angle contours are the lines of steepest ascent and descent on the terrain represented by the magnitude contours (see problem 5.26, page 144). This is a convenient feature to bear in mind when sketching contour maps. Again, the fact that the magnitude and angle contours intersect at right angles is reminiscent of the fact that equipotential surfaces and lines of force intersect at right angles in electrostatics. This relationship is not accidental (see problem 5.27, page 144) and is conveniently borne in mind when sketching contour maps.

3.4. Cross Sections of Contour Maps

The accurate drawing of a complete contour map for a vector function of a vector usually requires considerable calculation. It often happens however that this calculation is not strictly necessary for the purpose in mind. In the first place the general character of the contour map can often be appreciated with comparativly little calculation. For example, a function of the type appearing in Eq. (3.1) has poles at the positions $\mathbf{s}_1$, $\mathbf{s}_2$, ..., $\mathbf{s}_n$ in the $\mathbf{s}$ plane, and zeros at the positions $\mathbf{s}_1'$, $\mathbf{s}_2'$, ..., $\mathbf{s}_m'$. At each zero the terrain dips down to zero height in the manner indicated in Fig. 3.1, while at each pole the terrain rises to an indefinitely large height, in the manner indicated in Fig. 3.3. Thus, from a knowledge of the positions of the poles and zeros, and the known behavior of the terrain in the neighborhood of a pole and a zero, we may form a rough picture of the terrain associated with the function in Eq. (3.1). Thus, the general "lay of the land" may

* E. Jahnke, F. Emde, and F. Lösch, "Tables of Higher Functions," 6th ed. Mc Graw-Hill, New York, 1960.

frequently be visualized with far less calculation than would be required to plot a complete contour map.

The procedure just described for ascertaining, without detailed calculations, the general character of the terrain associated with a particular contour map is particularly convenient when detailed calculations are only required along a particular cross section of the map. In the analysis of linear oscillatory systems in physics and engineering it frequently happens that, when once the general character of the terrain associated with a contour map has been established, detailed calculations may be confined to the cross section of the map along the quadrature axis. Particular interest attaches therefore to calculating the way in which a vector function of a vector **s** varies along a particular line in the **s** plane.

3.5. Cross Section of a Contour Map along the Reference Axis

Before considering cross sections of contour maps along the quadrature axis it is appropriate to consider the cross sections along the reference axis. In the previous chapter we have seen that scalar algebra is the particular case of vector algebra when all vectors lie along the reference axis, positive numbers being represented by vectors in the reference direction and negative numbers by vectors in the opposite direction. Thus the cross section along the reference axis of the contour map of a particular function of a vector variable simply gives the behavior of the function when the independent variable is taken as a scalar quantity. Let us illustrate this with the aid of the function in Eq. (3.12).

If x is a scalar variable replacing the vector **s** in Eq. (3.12), we obtain on the right-hand side

$$\frac{1}{x} \tag{3.13}$$

and the graph representing this function is shown in Fig. 3.5. Let us restate this result in vector language. In vector language the variable x is represented by a vector of magnitude x in the reference direction if x is positive and by a vector of magnitude $-x$ in the direction opposite to the reference direction if x is negative. This means that

$$\mathbf{s} = \begin{cases} x \angle 0 & \text{if} \quad x > 0 \qquad (3.14) \\ -x \angle \pm\pi & \text{if} \quad x < 0 \qquad (3.15) \end{cases}$$

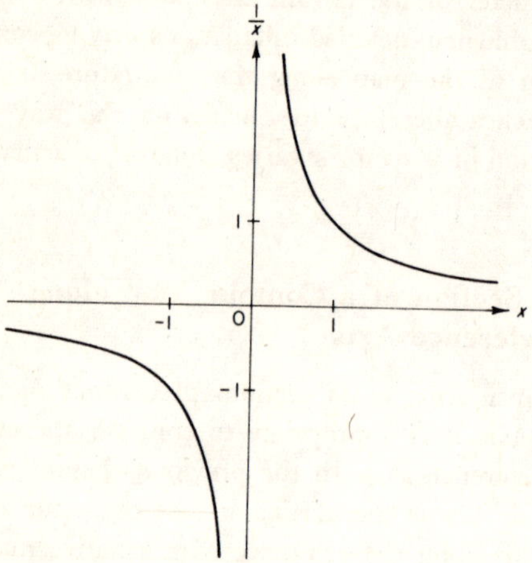

FIG. 3.5. Illustrating the graph of the function $1/x$.

The alternative sign in Eq. (3.15) implies that the direction opposite to the reference direction may be regarded as having a counterclockwise angle $+\pi$ with the reference direction or alternatively a counterclockwise angle $-\pi$. Let us now substitute the vector $\mathbf{s}$ given by Eqs. (3.14) and (3.15) into Eq. (3.12). We obtain

$$\mathbf{F}(\mathbf{s}) = \begin{cases} \dfrac{1}{x} \angle 0 & \text{if} \quad x > 0 \qquad (3.16) \\ -\dfrac{1}{x} \angle \mp\pi & \text{if} \quad x < 0. \qquad (3.17) \end{cases}$$

These equations give the cross section along the reference axis of the contour map illustrated in Fig. 3.4. The magnitude of the vector given by Eqs. (3.16) and (3.17) is shown as a function of x in Fig. 3.6(a), and the angle of the vector in Fig. 3.6(b).

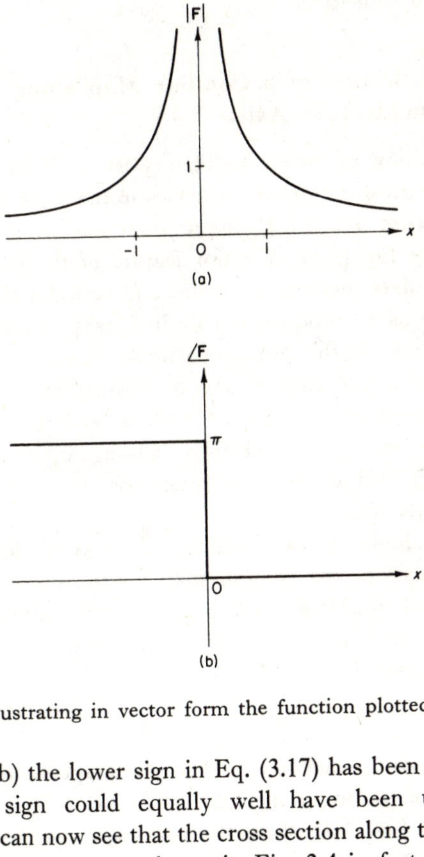

FIG. 3.6. Illustrating in vector form the function plotted in Fig. 3.5.

In Fig. 3.6(b) the lower sign in Eq. (3.17) has been chosen, but the upper sign could equally well have been used. From Fig. 3.6 we can now see that the cross section along the reference axis of the contour map shown in Fig. 3.4 in fact conveys the same information as the graph in Fig. 3.5. The change in the sign of the function in going from a positive value of x to a negative value of x in Fig. 3.5 is shown in Fig. 3.6 as a change from a vector making a zero angle with the reference direction to a vector making an angle π with the reference direction.

For any function of a vector variable, the cross section of the contour map along the reference axis simply gives the behavior of the function when the independent variable is replaced by a scalar quantity. This feature should be borne in mind when sketching contour maps.

3.6. Cross Section of a Contour Map along the Quadrature Axis

In the study of linear oscillatory systems in physics and engineering great importance attaches to the cross sections along the quadrature axis of algebraic functions of $\mathbf{s}$ of the type appearing in Eq. (3.1). A major feature of the design of such systems involves locating the poles and zeros in the $\mathbf{s}$ plane in such a way as to produce the desired cross section along the quadrature axis. In this process particular importance attaches to the effect of a pole close to the quadrature axis. As we move along the quadrature axis past such a pole, the terrain rises steeply to a maximum and then falls again, and this is the behavior required to describe resonance phenomena in linear oscillatory systems.

As an example let us examine the cross section along the quadrature axis of the contour map for the function given by Eq. (3.8) and illustrated in Fig. 3.3. Let us suppose that the pole at the point A in Fig. 3.3 is to the left of the quadrature axis as indicated. Let

$$\mathbf{s}_0 = -a + jb \tag{3.18}$$

where a is positive and is equal to the perpendicular distance from the pole A on to the quadrature axis. This situation is illustrated in Fig. 3.7, where the point $\mathbf{s}_0$ gives the location of the pole. When considering the cross section along the quadrature axis, the point $\mathbf{s}$ is located on the quadrature axis as shown in Fig. 3.7. Let y be the distance from the point $\mathbf{s}$ to the foot of the perpendicular from the pole onto the quadrature axis, and let y be measured positive in the positive direction of the quadrature axis. We can then see from the triangle in Fig. 3.7 that the vector from the point $\mathbf{s}_0$ to the point $\mathbf{s}$ has magnitude $(a^2 + y^2)^{1/2}$ and makes with the reference direction a counterclockwise angle whose tangent is y/a. Hence

$$\mathbf{s} - \mathbf{s}_0 = (a^2 + y^2)^{1/2} \angle \tan^{-1}\frac{y}{a}\,. \tag{3.19}$$

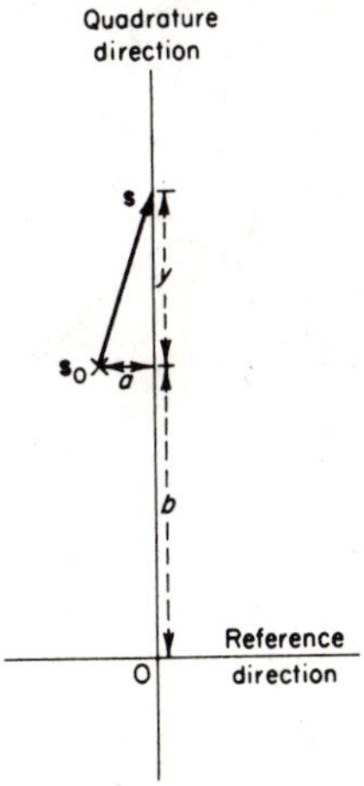

FIG. 3.7. Illustrating the derivation of the resonance curves.

This is the form taken by Eq. (3.3) in the circumstances illustrated in Fig. 3.7. Substitution from Eq. (3.19) into Eq. (3.8) then gives

$$\mathbf{F}(\mathbf{s}) = \frac{1}{(a^2 + y^2)^{1/2}} \angle -\tan^{-1}\frac{y}{a} \tag{3.20}$$

from which it follows that

$$|\,\mathbf{F}\,| = \frac{1}{(a^2 + y^2)^{1/2}} \tag{3.21}$$

and

$$\angle \mathbf{F} = -\tan^{-1}\frac{y}{a}\,. \tag{3.22}$$

The expression on the right-hand side of Eq. (3.21) is illustrated as a function of y in Fig. 3.8(a), while the expression on the right-hand side of Eq. (3.22) is illustrated as a function of y in Fig. 3.8(b). As we move along the quadrature axis in Fig. 3.7 in the positive direction, the variable y runs from $-\infty$ to $+\infty$, passing through the value zero at the foot of the perpendicular from the pole. As y increases from $-\infty$ to zero we are crossing the magnitude contours in Fig. 3.3 in the uphill direction. At

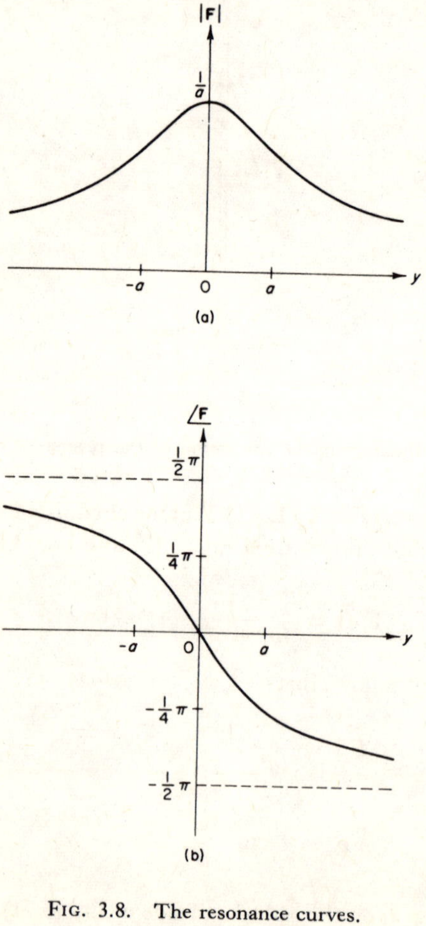

FIG. 3.8. The resonance curves.

the foot of the perpendicular from the pole we reach the highest point of the terrain on the quadrature axis. As y increases from zero to $+\infty$ we run downhill again. This is the behavior indicated in Fig. 3.8(a). Again, as we move along the quadrature axis in Fig. 3.3, we are crossing the angle contours. As y in Fig. 3.7 increases from $-\infty$ to zero, the markings on the angle contours in Fig. 3.3 vary from $\frac{1}{2}\pi$ to 0. As y increases from zero to $+\infty$ the markings on the angle contours vary from 0 to $-\frac{1}{2}\pi$. This is the behavior indicated in Fig. 3.8(b). Thus Fig. 3.8 gives the cross section along the quadrature axis of the contour map shown in Fig. 3.3.

The curves shown in Fig. 3.8 are of great importance for the analysis of resonant systems, and are known as the resonance curves. It will be noted that the magnitude curve in Fig. 3.8(a) has a maximum at $y = 0$, and that $|\mathbf{F}|$ has decreased to a fraction $1/\sqrt{2}$ of the maximum value at $y = \pm a$. This corresponds to the fact that when $y = \pm a$ in Fig. 3.7, the triangle indicated becomes isosceles. From this triangle it also follows that $\angle\mathbf{F}$ in Fig. 3.8(b) has the value $\frac{1}{4}\pi$ when $y = -a$ and the value $-\frac{1}{4}\pi$ when $y = +a$. It will be observed that the width of the maximum in Fig. 3.8(a) and the extent of the sloping linear behavior near $y = 0$ in Fig. 3.8(b) are both controlled by the value of a, that is, by the perpendicular distance of the pole from the quadrature axis in Fig. 3.7. When the pole is close to the quadrature axis, the value of a is small; we then have a sharp peak in Fig. 3.8(a), and a rapid switch in Fig. 3.8(b) from the angle $+\frac{1}{2}\pi$ to the angle $-\frac{1}{2}\pi$. As the pole recedes from the quadrature axis the maximum in Fig. 3.8(a) becomes wider and less pronounced, while the slope on the angle curve at $y = 0$ in Fig. 3.8(b) becomes more gradual.

3.7. Behavior of a Function near a Pole or Zero

It has been stated that the nature of the contour map for a function of $\mathbf{s}$ such as that in Eq. (3.1) may be visualized from the position vectors $\mathbf{s}_1, \mathbf{s}_2, \ldots, \mathbf{s}_n$ of the poles and the position vectors $\mathbf{s}_1', \mathbf{s}_2', \ldots, \mathbf{s}_m'$ of the zeros. In the neighborhood of a particular pole or zero the contour map is of the form shown in Fig. 3.3 or 3.1, respectively. However, in both cases it is usually necessary to rotate the contour maps shown in Fig. 3.3 and 3.1 around the pole or zero through a suitable angle and to make a suitable adjustment in the scale on which radial distance from the pole or zero is measured. The scale and orientation associated with each pole of a function and with each zero of the function are in general different.

As an example, let us consider the function

$$\mathbf{F}(\mathbf{s}) = \frac{2\mathbf{s}}{(\mathbf{s} - \mathbf{s}_1)(\mathbf{s} - \mathbf{s}_2)} \tag{3.23}$$

where

$$\mathbf{s}_1 = -a + \mathbf{j}b \tag{3.24}$$

and

$$\mathbf{s}_2 = -a - \mathbf{j}b. \tag{3.25}$$

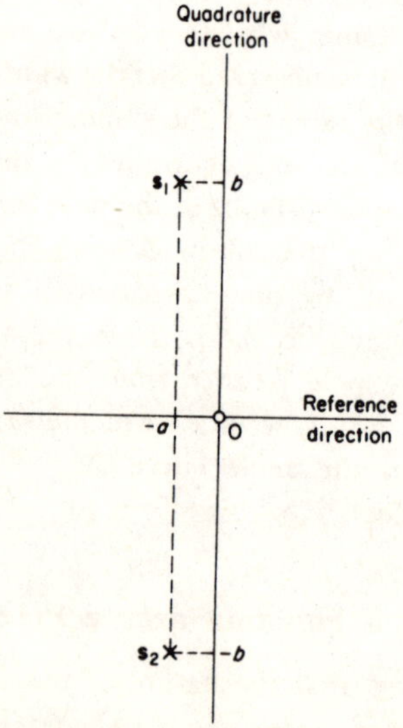

FIG. 3.9. Illustrating, for the function in Eq. (3.23), the poles at positions $\mathbf{s}_1$ and $\mathbf{s}_2$, and the zero at the origin.

We suppose that a and b are positive numbers and that a is small compared with b. For this function there are poles at the positions $\mathbf{s}_1$ and $\mathbf{s}_2$, and a zero at the origin, as indicated in Fig. 3.9. The complete contour map is shown in Fig. 3.10.

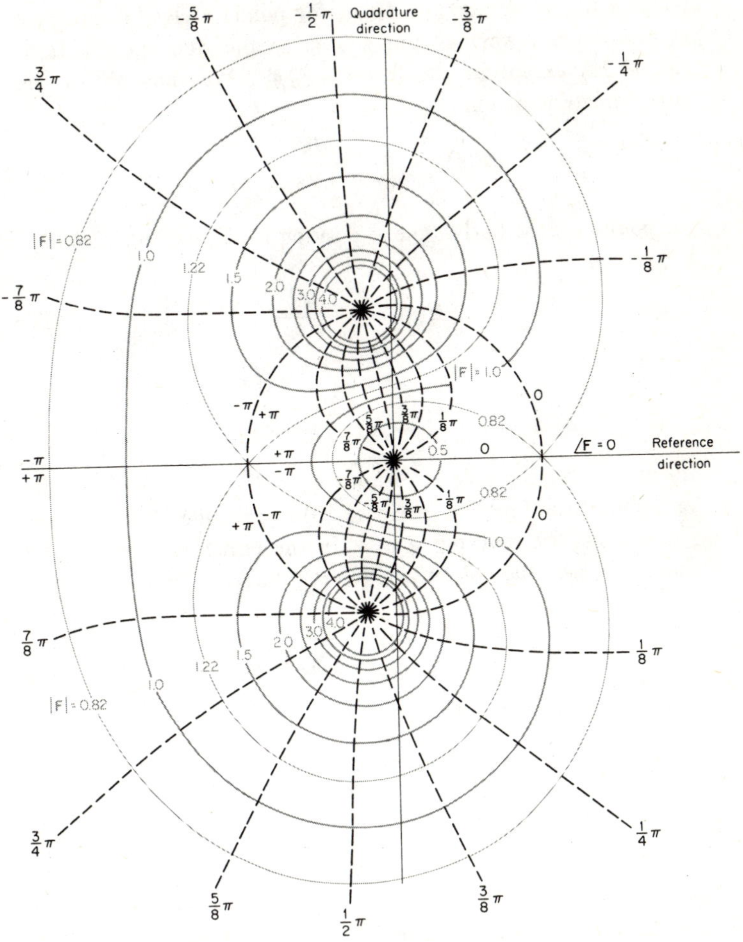

FIG. 3.10. Contour map for the function of $\mathbf{s}$ defined by Eqs. (3.23), (3.24), and (3.25).

In the neighborhood of the pole at position $\mathbf{s}_1$ in Figs. 3.9 and 3.10, the variation of the function in Eq. (3.23) is controlled almost entirely by the factor $\mathbf{s} - \mathbf{s}_1$ in the denominator. The extent by which $\mathbf{s}$ differs from $\mathbf{s}_1$ is vital in this factor but is unimportant in the factor $\mathbf{s} - \mathbf{s}_2$ in the denominator or in the factor $\mathbf{s}$ in the numerator. Thus, for points $\mathbf{s}$ close to the pole at position $\mathbf{s}_1$, we may put $\mathbf{s} = \mathbf{s}_1$ in the right-hand side of Eq. (3.23) except in the factor $\mathbf{s} - \mathbf{s}_1$. We thus obtain the approximate equation

$$\mathbf{F}(\mathbf{s}) = \frac{2\mathbf{s}_1}{(\mathbf{s} - \mathbf{s}_1)(\mathbf{s}_1 - \mathbf{s}_2)} \tag{3.26}$$

for points $\mathbf{s}$ close to the pole at position $\mathbf{s}_1$. Equation (3.26) may be written

$$\mathbf{F}(\mathbf{s}) = \frac{\mathbf{a}_1}{\mathbf{s} - \mathbf{s}_1} \tag{3.27}$$

where

$$\mathbf{a}_1 = \frac{2\mathbf{s}_1}{\mathbf{s}_1 - \mathbf{s}_2}. \tag{3.28}$$

Likewise, near the pole at position $\mathbf{s}_2$ in Figs. 3.9 and 3.10, the variation of the function in Eq. (3.23) is controlled by the factor $\mathbf{s} - \mathbf{s}_2$, and we may put $\mathbf{s} = \mathbf{s}_2$ in the remaining factors. We thus have, near the pole at position $\mathbf{s}_2$, the approximate equation

$$\mathbf{F}(\mathbf{s}) = \frac{2\mathbf{s}_2}{(\mathbf{s}_2 - \mathbf{s}_1)(\mathbf{s} - \mathbf{s}_2)} \tag{3.29}$$

which may be written

$$\mathbf{F}(\mathbf{s}) = \frac{\mathbf{a}_2}{\mathbf{s} - \mathbf{s}_2} \tag{3.30}$$

where

$$\mathbf{a}_2 = \frac{2\mathbf{s}_2}{\mathbf{s}_2 - \mathbf{s}_1}. \tag{3.31}$$

Again, the variation of the function in Eq. (3.23) in the neighborhood of the zero at the origin in Figs. 3.9 and 3.10 is controlled by the factor $\mathbf{s}$ in the numerator on the right-hand side of Eq.

(3.23), and we may put $\mathbf{s} = 0$ in the remaining factors. Near the zero at the origin we therefore have the approximate equation

$$\mathbf{F}(\mathbf{s}) = \frac{2\mathbf{s}}{(0 - \mathbf{s}_1)(0 - \mathbf{s}_2)} \tag{3.32}$$

which may be written

$$\mathbf{F}(\mathbf{s}) = \mathbf{a}_0\mathbf{s} \tag{3.33}$$

where

$$\mathbf{a}_0 = \frac{2}{\mathbf{s}_1\mathbf{s}_2}\,. \tag{3.34}$$

Into Eqs. (3.28), (3.31), and (3.34) we can now substitute the expressions for $\mathbf{s}_1$ and $\mathbf{s}_2$ given by Eqs. (3.24) and (3.25). If at the same time we assume that a is small compared with b as indicated in Figs. 3.9 and 3.10, we obtain the approximate equations

$$\mathbf{a}_1 = 1 \tag{3.35}$$

$$\mathbf{a}_2 = 1 \tag{3.36}$$

and

$$\mathbf{a}_0 = \frac{2}{b^2}\,. \tag{3.37}$$

Let us now compare Eq. (3.27) with Eq. (3.8). The fact that $\mathbf{s}_0$ in Eq. (3.8) is replaced by $\mathbf{s}_1$ in Eq. (3.27) merely implies that the position of the pole under consideration is the point $\mathbf{s}_1$ in Figs. 3.9 and 3.10. The vector $\mathbf{a}_1$ in the numerator of Eq. (3.27) implies, however, that the vector $1/(\mathbf{s} - \mathbf{s}_1)$ must be multiplied by $|\,\mathbf{a}_1\,|$ in magnitude and have its counterclockwise angle increased by $\angle\mathbf{a}_1$. This means that the behavior of the contour map in Fig. 3.10 near the pole at position $\mathbf{s}_1$ is of the type indicated in Fig. 3.3 provided that the magnitude markings are multiplied by $|\,\mathbf{a}_1\,|$ and the angle markings are increased by $\angle\mathbf{a}_1$, where $\mathbf{a}_1$ is given by Eq. (3.28). In the same way it follows from Eq. (3.30) that the behavior of the contour map in Fig. 3.10 in the neighborhood of the pole at position $\mathbf{s}_2$ is of the type shown in Fig. 3.3 provided that the magnitude markings multiplied by $|\mathbf{a}_2|$ and the angle markings increased by $\angle \mathbf{a}_2$, where $\mathbf{a}_2$ is given by Eq. (3.31). Likewise, comparison of Eqs. (3.33) and (3.7) shows that the behavior of the contour map in Fig. 3.10 in the neighborhood of the zero at the origin is of the type shown in Fig. 3.2 provided that the magnitude markings are multiplied by $|\mathbf{a}_0|$ and the angle markings are increased by $\angle \mathbf{a}_0$, where $\mathbf{a}_0$ is given by Eq. (3.34). Using the approximate expressions for $\mathbf{a}_1$, $\mathbf{a}_2$, and $\mathbf{a}_0$ given in Eqs. (3.35), (3.36), and (3.37), we may verify all of these features in the contour map shown in Fig. 3.10.

The cross section along the quadrature axis of the contour map shown in Fig. 3.10 is illustrated in Fig. 3.11. The variable y in Fig. 3.11 is distance measured from the origin in Fig. 3.10 along the quadrature axis in the positive quadrature direction. As we move along the quadrature axis in Figs. 3.9 and 3.10 we pass close to the pole at position $\mathbf{s}_2$ as y increases through the value $-b$, and close to the pole at position $\mathbf{s}_1$ as y increases through the value $+b$. The behavior in Fig. 3.11 as we pass each pole is described by the resonance curves in Fig. 3.8.

For any algebraic function of $\mathbf{s}$ of the type appearing in Eq. (3.1) the behavior in the neighborhood of the poles and zeros is obtained as follows: Consider first the pole at position $\mathbf{s}_1$. The variation in the neighborhood of this pole is controlled by factor $\mathbf{s} - \mathbf{s}_1$ in the denominator on the right-hand side of Eq. (3.1). Near this pole we may put $\mathbf{s} = \mathbf{s}_1$ in all the other factors. The behavior near the pole at position $\mathbf{s}_1$ is therefore given by

$$\mathbf{F}(\mathbf{s}) = \frac{\mathbf{a}_1}{\mathbf{s} - \mathbf{s}_1} \tag{3.38}$$

where

$$\mathbf{a}_1 = \frac{(\mathbf{s}_1 - \mathbf{s}_1')(\mathbf{s}_1 - \mathbf{s}_2') \cdots (\mathbf{s}_1 - \mathbf{s}_m')}{(\mathbf{s}_1 - \mathbf{s}_2)(\mathbf{s}_1 - \mathbf{s}_3) \cdots (\mathbf{s}_1 - \mathbf{s}_n)} \tag{3.39}$$

and similar statements apply to the other poles. In the neighborhood of the zero at location $\mathbf{s}_1'$, the variation of the function is controlled by the factor $\mathbf{s} - \mathbf{s}_1'$ in the numerator on the right-hand side of Eq. (3.1). Near this zero we may put $\mathbf{s} = \mathbf{s}_1'$

in all the other factors. The behavior in the neighborhood of the zero at position $\mathbf{s}_1'$ is therefore given by

$$\mathbf{F}(\mathbf{s}) = \mathbf{a}_1'(\mathbf{s} - \mathbf{s}_1') \tag{3.40}$$

where

$$\mathbf{a}_1' = \frac{(\mathbf{s}_1' - \mathbf{s}_2')(\mathbf{s}_1' - \mathbf{s}_3') \cdots (\mathbf{s}_1' - \mathbf{s}_m')}{(\mathbf{s}_1' - \mathbf{s}_1)(\mathbf{s}_1' - \mathbf{s}_2) \cdots (\mathbf{s}_1' - \mathbf{s}_n)} \tag{3.41}$$

and similar statements apply to the other zeros.

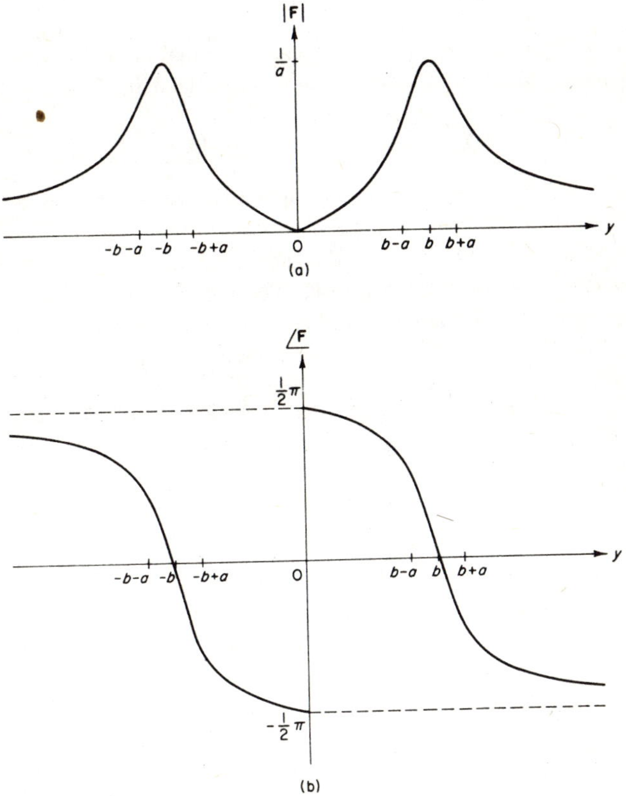

FIG. 3.11. Illustrating the cross section along the quadrature axis of the contour map shown in Fig. 3.10: (a) in magnitude, and (b) in angle.

3.8. Analysis into Partial Fractions

The process described in the previous section for finding the behavior of an algebraic function of a vector in the neighborhood of its poles is of considerable practical importance. This process is often conveniently carried out by the technique known as analysis into partial fractions. Let us consider an algebraic function of **s** of the form

$$\frac{\mathbf{N}(\mathbf{s})}{\mathbf{P}(\mathbf{s})} \tag{3.42}$$

where **N**(**s**) and **P**(**s**) are polynominal functions of **s**. Let the polynominal in the denominator be factorized in the form

$$\mathbf{P}(\mathbf{s}) = (\mathbf{s} - \mathbf{s}_1)(\mathbf{s} - \mathbf{s}_2) \cdots (\mathbf{s} - \mathbf{s}_n) \tag{3.43}$$

where $\mathbf{s}_1$, $\mathbf{s}_2$, ..., $\mathbf{s}_n$ are fixed vectors that we suppose to be all different. If the polynominal in the numerator in expression (3.42) were also factorized, the algebraic function of **s** would take the form shown in Eq. (3.1). The highest power of **s** in the numerator in expression (3.42) may be equal to or greater than the highest power of **s** in the denominator. In this case we can divide the denominator into the numerator obtaining a quotient polynominal **Q**(**s**) and a remainder polynominal **R**(**s**). Expression (3.42) then takes the form

$$\mathbf{Q}(\mathbf{s}) + \frac{\mathbf{R}(\mathbf{s})}{\mathbf{P}(\mathbf{s})} . \tag{3.44}$$

The highest power of **s** in the remainder polynominal **R**(**s**) is now less than the highest power of **s** in the denominator **P**(**s**). It is to the algebraic fraction

$$\frac{\mathbf{R}(\mathbf{s})}{\mathbf{P}(\mathbf{s})} \tag{3.45}$$

that the process of analysis into partial fractions is applied. If both the numerator and denominator in expression (3.45) are factorized, this algebraic fraction takes the form shown in Eq. (3.1) with m less than n.

Substitution for $\mathbf{P}(\mathbf{s})$ from Eq. (3.43) into expression (3.45) shows that the algebraic fraction to be analyzed into partial fractions may be written

$$\frac{\mathbf{R}(\mathbf{s})}{(\mathbf{s}-\mathbf{s}_1)(\mathbf{s}-\mathbf{s}_2)\cdots(\mathbf{s}-\mathbf{s}_n)} \tag{3.46}$$

where the highest power of $\mathbf{s}$ in $\mathbf{R}(\mathbf{s})$ is less than n.

The process of analysis into partial fractions involves finding constant vectors $\mathbf{a}_1$, $\mathbf{a}_2$, ..., $\mathbf{a}_n$ such that expression (3.46) can be written in the form

$$\frac{\mathbf{a}_1}{\mathbf{s}-\mathbf{s}_1}+\frac{\mathbf{a}_2}{\mathbf{s}-\mathbf{s}_2}+\cdots+\frac{\mathbf{a}_n}{\mathbf{s}-\mathbf{s}_n}. \tag{3.47}$$

Each term in expression (3.47) is called a partial fraction, and the sum of all the partial fractions reproduces the algebraic fraction specified in expression (3.46).

Let us illustrate the process of finding the constant vectors $\mathbf{a}_1$, $\mathbf{a}_2$, ..., $\mathbf{a}_n$ associated with the partial fractions in expression (3.47) for the case $n = 3$. We then have to find constant vectors $\mathbf{a}_1$, $\mathbf{a}_2$, and $\mathbf{a}_3$ such that, for all vectors $\mathbf{s}$,

$$\frac{\mathbf{R}(\mathbf{s})}{(\mathbf{s}-\mathbf{s}_1)(\mathbf{s}-\mathbf{s}_2)(\mathbf{s}-\mathbf{s}_3)}=\frac{\mathbf{a}_1}{\mathbf{s}-\mathbf{s}_1}+\frac{\mathbf{a}_2}{\mathbf{s}-\mathbf{s}_2}+\frac{\mathbf{a}_3}{\mathbf{s}-\mathbf{s}_3}. \tag{3.48}$$

The procedure is to multiply both sides of Eq. (3.48) by the denominator in the expression on the left-hand side, thereby obtaining

$$\mathbf{R}(\mathbf{s}) = \mathbf{a}_1(\mathbf{s}-\mathbf{s}_2)(\mathbf{s}-\mathbf{s}_3)+\mathbf{a}_2(\mathbf{s}-\mathbf{s}_1)(\mathbf{s}-\mathbf{s}_3) + \mathbf{a}_3(\mathbf{s}-\mathbf{s}_1)(\mathbf{s}-\mathbf{s}_2). \tag{3.49}$$

Since Eq. (3.49) is to be true for all vectors $\mathbf{s}$, we may substitute into the equation any expressions for $\mathbf{s}$ that may be convenient. To determine the constant vector $\mathbf{a}_1$ it is convenient to put $\mathbf{s} = \mathbf{s}_1$. This removes the terms involving $\mathbf{a}_2$ and $\mathbf{a}_3$, so that we obtain

$$\mathbf{R}(\mathbf{s}_1) = \mathbf{a}_1(\mathbf{s}_1-\mathbf{s}_2)(\mathbf{s}_1-\mathbf{s}_3). \tag{3.50}$$

In the same way, by putting $\mathbf{s} = \mathbf{s}_2$ in Eq. (3.49) we remove the terms involving $\mathbf{a}_1$ and $\mathbf{a}_3$ and obtain

$$\mathbf{R}(\mathbf{s}_2) = \mathbf{a}_2(\mathbf{s}_2 - \mathbf{s}_1)(\mathbf{s}_2 - \mathbf{s}_3). \tag{3.51}$$

Finally, by putting $\mathbf{s} = \mathbf{s}_3$ in Eq. (3.49), we obtain

$$\mathbf{R}(\mathbf{s}_3) = \mathbf{a}_3(\mathbf{s}_3 - \mathbf{s}_1)(\mathbf{s}_3 - \mathbf{s}_2). \tag{3.52}$$

It follows from Eqs. (3.50), (3.51), and (3.52) that the constant vectors in the partial fraction analysis in Eq. (3.48) are

$$\mathbf{a}_1 = \frac{\mathbf{R}(\mathbf{s}_1)}{(\mathbf{s}_1 - \mathbf{s}_2)(\mathbf{s}_1 - \mathbf{s}_3)} \tag{3.53}$$

$$\mathbf{a}_2 = \frac{\mathbf{R}(\mathbf{s}_2)}{(\mathbf{s}_2 - \mathbf{s}_1)(\mathbf{s}_2 - \mathbf{s}_3)} \tag{3.54}$$

$$\mathbf{a}_3 = \frac{\mathbf{R}(\mathbf{s}_3)}{(\mathbf{s}_3 - \mathbf{s}_1)(\mathbf{s}_3 - \mathbf{s}_1)}\,. \tag{3.55}$$

Substitution of these values for $\mathbf{a}_1$, $\mathbf{a}_2$, and $\mathbf{a}_3$ into Eq. (3.48) gives

$$\begin{aligned}\frac{\mathbf{R}(\mathbf{s})}{(\mathbf{s} - \mathbf{s}_1)(\mathbf{s} - \mathbf{s}_2)(\mathbf{s} - \mathbf{s}_3)} &= \frac{\mathbf{R}(\mathbf{s}_1)}{(\mathbf{s} - \mathbf{s}_1)(\mathbf{s}_1 - \mathbf{s}_2)(\mathbf{s}_1 - \mathbf{s}_3)} \\ &+ \frac{\mathbf{R}(\mathbf{s}_2)}{(\mathbf{s}_2 - \mathbf{s}_1)(\mathbf{s} - \mathbf{s}_2)(\mathbf{s}_2 - \mathbf{s}_3)} \\ &+ \frac{\mathbf{R}(\mathbf{s}_3)}{(\mathbf{s}_3 - \mathbf{s}_1)(\mathbf{s}_3 - \mathbf{s}_2)(\mathbf{s} - \mathbf{s}_3)}\,.\end{aligned} \tag{3.56}$$

This partial fraction analysis is valid for all magnitudes and directions for the vector $\mathbf{s}$. It should be noted that the partial fraction analysis presented in Eq. (3.56) may be written down at sight by the following procedure:

(1) Write down the expression to be analyzed as many times as there are factors in the denominator.

(2) In the first term replace $\mathbf{s}$ by $\mathbf{s}_1$ except in the factor $\mathbf{s} - \mathbf{s}_1$.

(3) In the second term replace $\mathbf{s}$ by $\mathbf{s}_2$ except in the factor $\mathbf{s} - \mathbf{s}_2$.

(4) Apply this procedure to all the terms and add them together.

We then have the required analysis into partial fractions.

It should be noted that each term of the partial fraction analysis gives the behavior of the original algebraic function of $\mathbf{s}$ in the neighborhood of one of its poles. In fact the procedure just described for calculating the constant vector $\mathbf{a}_1$ in the partial fraction analysis simply constitutes an application of Eq. (3.39).

The procedure described in this section for analysis into partial fractions fails if two of the fixed vectors $\mathbf{s}_1, \mathbf{s}_2, \ldots, \mathbf{s}_n$ in expression (3.46) are identical. This is a situation that may be dealt with when it occurs as follows: Let us suppose, for example, that $\mathbf{s}_1$ and $\mathbf{s}_2$ are each equal to $\mathbf{s}_0$. We then replace the first two terms in expression (3.47) by

$$\frac{\mathbf{a}_1}{(\mathbf{s} - \mathbf{s}_0)^2} + \frac{\mathbf{a}_2}{\mathbf{s} - \mathbf{s}_0}. \qquad (3.57)$$

If the first p of the vectors $\mathbf{s}_1, \mathbf{s}_2, \ldots, \mathbf{s}_n$ in expression (3.46) are each equal to $\mathbf{s}_0$, we replace the first p terms in the partial fraction analysis by

$$\frac{\mathbf{a}_1}{(\mathbf{s} - \mathbf{s}_0)^p} + \frac{\mathbf{a}_2}{(\mathbf{s} - \mathbf{s}_0)^{p-1}} + \cdots + \frac{\mathbf{a}_p}{\mathbf{s} - \mathbf{s}_0}. \qquad (3.58)$$

The coefficients are then determined by taking a common denominator as in Eq. (3.49) and substituting suitable values for $\mathbf{s}$ to obtain equations for the coefficients.

3.9. Application of Partial Fraction Analysis

As an example of partial fraction analysis let us analyze into partial fractions the function of $\mathbf{s}$ given in Eq. (3.23) and use the result to derive the cross section along the quadrature axis illustrated in Fig. 3.11. We assume that $\mathbf{s}_1$ and $\mathbf{s}_2$ are given by

Eqs. (3.24) and (3.25), so that $\mathbf{s}_1$ and $\mathbf{s}_2$ are unequal. Applying the rule for analysis into partial fractions derived in the previous section, we write the expression on the right-hand side of Eq. (3.23) down twice, on the first occasion replacing $\mathbf{s}$ by $\mathbf{s}_1$ except in the factor $\mathbf{s} - \mathbf{s}_1$, and on the second occasion replacing $\mathbf{s}$ by $\mathbf{s}_2$ except in the factor $\mathbf{s} - \mathbf{s}_2$. In this way we see that Eq. (3.23) may be replaced by

$$\mathbf{F}(\mathbf{s}) = \frac{2\mathbf{s}_1}{(\mathbf{s} - \mathbf{s}_1)(\mathbf{s}_1 - \mathbf{s}_2)} + \frac{2\mathbf{s}_2}{(\mathbf{s}_2 - \mathbf{s}_1)(\mathbf{s} - \mathbf{s}_2)} \cdot \qquad (3.59)$$

If we use the expressions for $\mathbf{a}_1$ and $\mathbf{a}_2$ given in Eqs. (3.28) and (3.31), respectively, Eq. (3.59) may be written

$$\mathbf{F}(\mathbf{s}) = \frac{\mathbf{a}_1}{\mathbf{s} - \mathbf{s}_1} + \frac{\mathbf{a}_2}{\mathbf{s} - \mathbf{s}_2} \cdot \qquad (3.60)$$

The first partial fraction in Eq. (3.59) or (3.60) gives the behavior of the contour map shown in Fig. 3.10 in the neighborhood of the pole at position $\mathbf{s}_1$. The second partial fraction in Eq. (3.59) or (3.60) gives the behavior of the contour map in the neighborhood of the pole at position $\mathbf{s}_2$. The zero in Fig. 3.10 arises from the fact that, at the origin, the two partial fractions in Eq. (3.59) represent vectors that are equal in magnitude and opposite in direction.

If it is assumed that the two poles are close to the quadrature axis as indicated in Fig. 3.10, the numerical value of a in Eqs. (3.24) and (3.25) is small compared with the numerical value of b, and we may use the approximate expressions for $\mathbf{a}_1$ and $\mathbf{a}_2$ given in Eqs. (3.35) and (3.36). In these circumstances Eq. (3.60) may be written

$$\mathbf{F}(\mathbf{s}) = \frac{1}{\mathbf{s} - \mathbf{s}_1} + \frac{1}{\mathbf{s} - \mathbf{s}_2} \cdot \qquad (3.61)$$

In this approximate form the two partial fractions do not balance precisely at the origin; however the first and second partial fractions in Eq. (3.61) still represent quite well the behavior of the contour map in Fig. 3.10 in the neighborhood of the poles at positions $\mathbf{s}_1$ and $\mathbf{s}_2$, respectively.

When considering the cross section along the quadrature axis, the point **s** is located on the quadrature axis as shown in Fig. 3.12. Since the distance of the point **s** along the quadrature

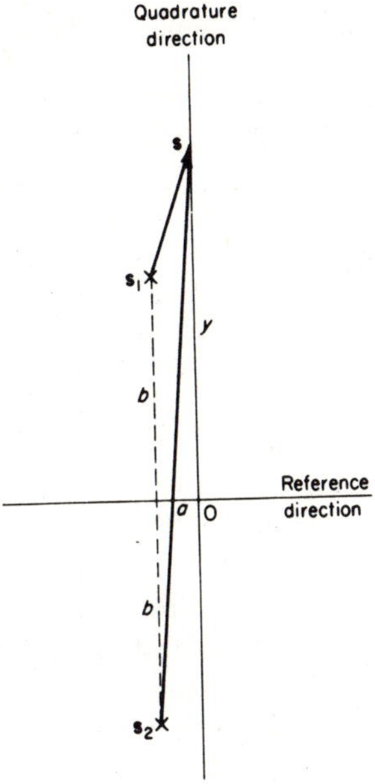

FIG. 3.12. Illustrating the derivation of Fig. 3.11 using partial fractions.

axis from the origin is y, the distances from the point **s** to the feet of the perpendiculars from the poles $\mathbf{s}_1$ and $\mathbf{s}_2$ are $y - b$ and $y + b$, respectively. From the geometry of Fig. 3.12 we may write down expressions for the vectors $\mathbf{s} - \mathbf{s}_1$ and $\mathbf{s} - \mathbf{s}_2$ by the method used for deriving Eq. (3.19) from Fig. 3.7. In this way we obtain

$$\mathbf{s} - \mathbf{s}_1 = [a^2 + (y - b)^2]^{1/2} \angle \tan^{-1} \frac{y - b}{a} \tag{3.62}$$

and

$$\mathbf{s} - \mathbf{s}_2 = [a^2 + (y + b)^2]^{1/2} \angle \tan^{-1} \frac{y + b}{a} . \tag{3.63}$$

The behavior of the curves shown in Fig. 3.11 for values of y in the neighborhood of b is obtained by substituting from Eq. (3.62) into the first of the partial fractions on the right-hand side of Eq. (3.61). In this way we obtain for the cross section along the quadrature axis for values of y near b the approximate equation

$$\mathbf{F}(\mathbf{s}) = \frac{1}{[a^2 + (y - b)^2]^{1/2}} \angle -\tan^{-1}\frac{y - b}{a} \tag{3.64}$$

from which we deduce that

$$|\mathbf{F}| = \frac{1}{[a^2 + (y - b)^2]^{1/2}} \tag{3.65}$$

and

$$\angle\mathbf{F} = -\tan^{-1}\frac{y - b}{a}. \tag{3.66}$$

Equation (3.65) gives the form of the curve in Fig. 3.11(a) for values of y near b, while Eq. (3.66) gives the form of the curve in Fig. 3.11(b) for values of y near b. In the same way the behavior of the curves in Fig. 3.11 for values of y in the neighborhood of $-b$ is obtained by substituting from Eq. (3.63) into the second of the partial fractions on the right-hand side of Eq. (3.61). We obtain approximately

$$\mathbf{F}(\mathbf{s}) = \frac{1}{[a^2 + (y + b)^2]^{1/2}} \angle -\tan^{-1}\frac{y + b}{a} \tag{3.67}$$

leading to

$$|\mathbf{F}| = \frac{1}{[a^2 + (y + b)^2]^{1/2}} \tag{3.68}$$

and

$$\angle\mathbf{F} = -\tan^{-1}\frac{y + b}{a}. \tag{3.69}$$

By using the partial fraction analysis given in Eq. (3.60), we may plot the curves shown in Fig. 3.11 accurately for all values of y. The first partial fraction on the right-hand side of Eq. (3.60) is the planar product of the vector $\mathbf{a}_1$ given by Eq. (3.28) and the vector appearing on the right-hand side of Eq. (3.64). Likewise the second partial fraction on the right-hand side of Eq. (3.60) is the planar product of the vectors $\mathbf{a}_2$ given by Eq. (3.31) and the vector appearing on the right-hand side of Eq. (3.67). In this way we may calculate accurately the variation with y of the two vectors constituting the two partial fractions in Eq. (3.60), and by taking the vector sum we obtain the curve shown in Fig. 3.11 without making any approximations. In practice, however, it is usually for values of y in the neighborhood of b and $-b$ that the curves in Fig. 3.11 are of greatest interest. This behavior may be obtained directly from the resonance curves shown in Fig. 3.8 and described in Section 3.6, and is represented analytically by Eqs. (3.64) through (3.69).

Summarizing Exercises

3.1. Describe the use of contour maps to illustrate in magnitude and direction how a vector function of a vector depends upon the magnitude and direction of the independent variable. Illustrate the process for the functions $\mathbf{s} - \mathbf{s}_0$ and $1/(\mathbf{s}-\mathbf{s}_0)$ where $\mathbf{s}$ is a variable vector and $\mathbf{s}_0$ is a fixed vector.

3.2. A fixed vector $\mathbf{s}_0$ has a negative reference component $-a$ and a quadrature component b that may be either positive or negative. Illustrate graphically the variation in magnitude and direction of the vector $1/(\mathbf{s} - \mathbf{s}_0)$ as the tip of the vector $\mathbf{s}$ moves along the quadrature axis in the $\mathbf{s}$ plane.

3.3. Explain what are meant by the resonance curves. In the previous exercise explain what controls the location and width of the resonance curves. Derive analytical expressions for the resonance curves.

3.4. For the function of $\mathbf{s}$ given by

$$\mathbf{F}(\mathbf{s}) = \frac{(\mathbf{s} - \mathbf{s}_1')(\mathbf{s} - \mathbf{s}_2') \cdots (\mathbf{s} - \mathbf{s}_m')}{(\mathbf{s} - \mathbf{s}_1)(\mathbf{s} - \mathbf{s}_2) \cdots (\mathbf{s} - \mathbf{s}_n)}$$

where $\mathbf{s}_1, \mathbf{s}_2, \ldots, \mathbf{s}_n,\ \mathbf{s}_1', \mathbf{s}_2', \ldots, \mathbf{s}_m'$ are unequal fixed vectors, show that, near the pole at location $\mathbf{s}_1$, we may write

$$\mathbf{F}(\mathbf{s}) = \frac{\mathbf{a}_1}{\mathbf{s} - \mathbf{s}_1}$$

approximately. Show also that, near the zero at location $\mathbf{s}_1'$, we may write

$$\mathbf{F}(\mathbf{s}) = \mathbf{a}_1'(\mathbf{s} - \mathbf{s}_1')$$

approximately. Explain how to calculate the vectors $\mathbf{a}_1$ and $\mathbf{a}_1'$.

3.5. Explain what is meant by analysis into partial fractions of the quotient of two polynomial functions of a vector. Write down at sight the partial fraction analysis of

$$\frac{\mathbf{R}(\mathbf{s})}{(\mathbf{s} - \mathbf{s}_1)(\mathbf{s} - \mathbf{s}_2) \cdots (\mathbf{s} - \mathbf{s}_n)}$$

where $\mathbf{s}_1, \mathbf{s}_2, \ldots, \mathbf{s}_n$ are unequal fixed vectors, and $\mathbf{R}(\mathbf{s})$ is a polynomial function in which the highest power of $\mathbf{s}$ is less than n. Justify the partial fraction analysis written down.

3.6. Explain how to perform a partial fraction analysis of an algebraic function whose denominator contains a repeated factor.

3.7. Analyze into partial fractions the function of $\mathbf{s}$ given by

$$\mathbf{F}(\mathbf{s}) = \frac{2\mathbf{s}}{(\mathbf{s} + a)^2 + b^2}$$

where a and b are positive. Sketch a contour map in the $\mathbf{s}$ plane for the magnitude and angle of $\mathbf{F}(\mathbf{s})$. Sketch curves to illustrate the cross section of the contour map along the quadrature axis. Explain the relation of these curves to the resonance curves when a is small compared with b.

CHAPTER 4

THE EXPONENTIAL FUNCTION OF A VECTOR

4.1. Introduction

In Chapter 1 we saw the importance of representing a sinusoidal oscillation as the reference component of a uniformly rotating vector. Corresponding to the replacement of the sinusoidal graph in Fig. 1.1 by the rotating vector in Fig. 1.3, we need to find an appropriate analytical representation of the rotating vector to replace the sinusoidal function in Eq. (1.1).

In Chapters 2 and 3 we have seen that an algebraic function of a vector **s** gives a new vector, the magnitude and direction of which vary with the magnitude and direction of **s**. This statement is true not only for algebraic functions but also for a wide range of other functions. Such functions include the exponential function. It is by ascertaining the significance of the exponential function of a vector that we shall be able to obtain an analytical representation of the rotating vectors involved in the study of oscillations.

4.2. Contour Map for the Exponential Function of a Vector

Let us consider the vector obtained by performing the summation

$$1 + \mathbf{s} + \frac{1}{2!}\mathbf{s}^2 + \frac{1}{3!}\mathbf{s}^3 + \cdots \qquad (4.1)$$

where $n!$ is the factorial function and denotes $n(n-1)(n-2)\cdots 1$. The summation in Eq. (4.1) is an infinite series of which the first n terms constitute a polynominal function of $\mathbf{s}$ of the type discussed in Chapters 2 and 3. The first term in expression (4.1) is a unit vector in the reference direction. The remaining terms are vectors that can be evaluated by the planar product rule when the vector $\mathbf{s}$ is known. The series of vectors represented by the terms in expression (4.1) may then be summed, thereby arriving at a resultant vector. This process is illustrated in Fig. 4.1 for the case when

$$\mathbf{s} = \frac{1}{2} \angle \frac{\pi}{3}. \tag{4.2}$$

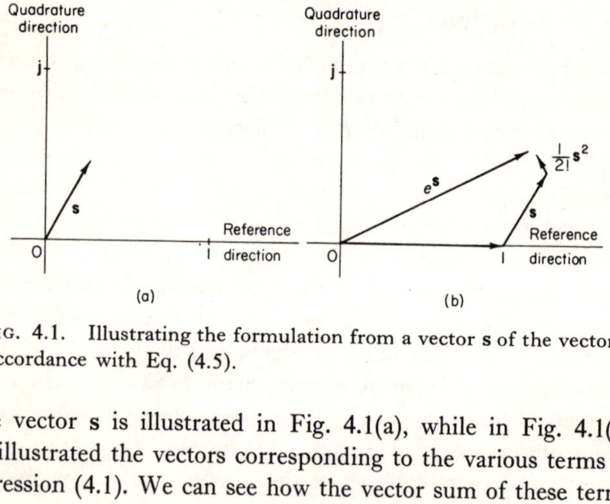

FIG. 4.1. Illustrating the formulation from a vector $\mathbf{s}$ of the vector $e^{\mathbf{s}}$ in accordance with Eq. (4.5).

The vector $\mathbf{s}$ is illustrated in Fig. 4.1(a), while in Fig. 4.1(b) are illustrated the vectors corresponding to the various terms in expression (4.1). We can see how the vector sum of these terms is converging to the resultant vector indicated.

In scalar algebra the infinite series

$$1 + x + \frac{1}{2!} x^2 + \frac{1}{3!} x^3 + \cdots \tag{4.3}$$

represents the exponential function of the scalar quantity x, and we write

$$e^x = 1 + x + \frac{1}{2!} x^2 + \frac{1}{3!} x^3 + \cdots . \tag{4.4}$$

In vector algebra the same terminology and notation are used. The resultant vector calculated from the infinite series in expression (4.1) in the manner illustrated in Fig. 4.1 is therefore denoted by $e^{\mathbf{s}}$, and we write

$$e^{\mathbf{s}} = 1 + \mathbf{s} + \frac{1}{2!}\,\mathbf{s}^2 + \frac{1}{3!}\,\mathbf{s}^3 + \cdots . \tag{4.5}$$

The vector formed by carrying out the summation on the right-hand side of Eq. (4.5) in the manner illustrated in Fig. 4.1 is described as the exponential function of the vector **s**.

As the vector **s** in Fig. 4.1(a) varies in magnitude and direction, so also does the resultant vector $e^{\mathbf{s}}$ in Fig. 4.1(b). This variation is conveniently represented by means of a contour map in the **s** plane in the manner described in the previous chapter. The contour map for the exponential function of the vector **s** is shown in Fig. 4.2. The vector $\overrightarrow{OP}$ in Fig. 4.2 indicates a typical magnitude and direction for the vector **s**. The corresponding vector $e^{\mathbf{s}}$ then has a magnitude equal to the marking on the magnitude contour through the point P and makes a counterclockwise angle with the reference direction equal to the marking on the angle contour through the point P.

The magnitude contours in Fig. 4.2 are parallel to the quadrature axis and become more closely spaced as we move to the right of the diagram. The corresponding terrain has an indefinitely small height at the extreme left of the diagram and rises steadily as we move to the right, with an ever increasing slope. The height of the terrain is unity on the quadrature axis and become indefinitely large at the extreme right of the diagram. The angle contours intersect the magnitude contours at right angles and are equally spaced. Thus, as we move to the right in Fig. 4.2 along a line parallel to the reference axis, the angle of the vector $e^{\mathbf{s}}$ remains fixed while the magnitude increases. On the other hand, as we move toward the top of the page in Fig. 4.2 along a line parallel to the quadrature axis, the magnitude of the vector $e^{\mathbf{s}}$ remains constant while its counterclockwise angle with the reference direction steadily increases. This means that, as the tip of the vector **s** in Fig. 4.2 moves along a line parallel to the quadrature axis, the corresponding vector e^s remains constant in magnitude but rotates. Moreover, if the point P moves with uniform velocity parallel to the quadrature axis, the rate of rotation of the vector e^s is uniform since the angle contours in Fig. 4.2 are equally spaced. This demonstrates the ability of the exponential function of a vector to represent a rotating vector.

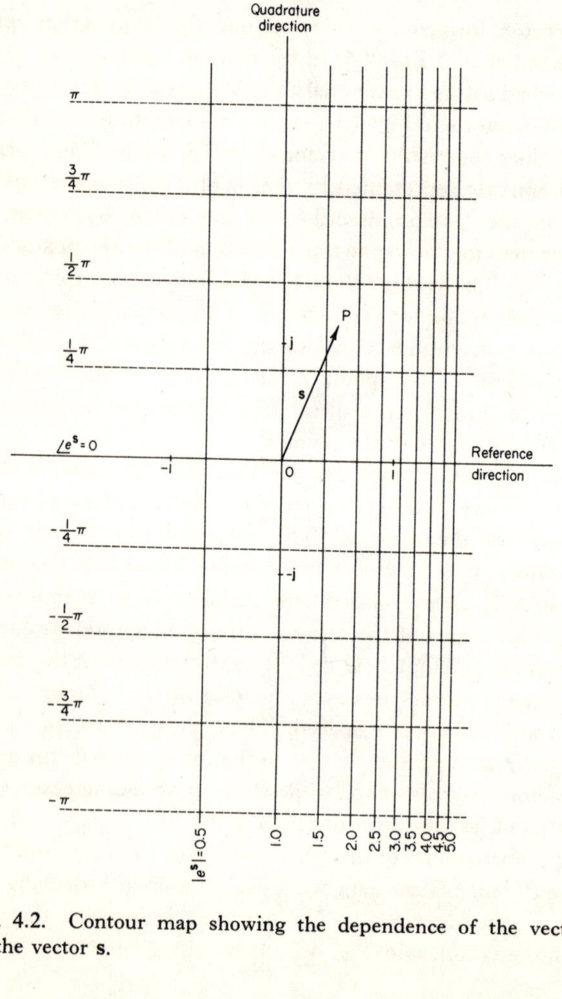

FIG. 4.2. Contour map showing the dependence of the vector e upon the vector **s**.

The contour map for the exponential function illustrated in Fig. 4.2 may be constructed by performing the operation illustrated in Fig. 4.1 for a large number of magnitudes and directions for the vector **s**. However, the contour map illustrated in Fig. 4.2 has a number of special features the truth of which can be established analytically. Thus, we shall prove analytically in Section 4.6 that the magnitude contours are straight lines parallel to the quadrature axis, while the angle contours are equally spaced straight lines parallel to the reference axis. To do so it is convenient initially to consider the cross sections of the contour map along the reference and quadrature axes. The cross section along the quadrature axis is considered in the following section. The cross section along the reference axis is obtained as follows: If the reference and quadrature components of the vector **s** in Fig. 4.2 are denoted by x and y, we have on the reference axis

$$\mathbf{s} = x + \mathrm{j}0. \tag{4.6}$$

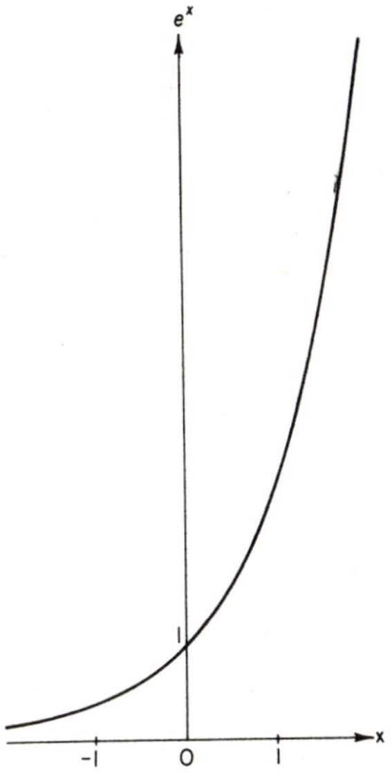

FIG. 4.3. Graph of the scalar exponential function.

In these circumstances Eq. (4.5) reduces to Eq. (4.4), and we have

$$e^{\mathbf{s}} = e^{x} \angle 0. \tag{4.7}$$

It follows from Eq. (4.7) that the reference axis is the angle contour marked zero as shown in Fig. 4.2, while the cross section of the terrain along the reference axis is given by the graph of the scalar exponential function illustrated in Fig. 4.3.

4.3. The Exponential Representation of a Unit Vector Pointing in Any Direction

Let us now consider the cross section of the contour map in Fig. 4.2 along the quadrature axis. If the reference and quadrature components of the vector **s** are x and y, we have on the quadrature axis

$$\mathbf{s} = 0 + \mathrm{j}y. \tag{4.8}$$

The marking on the magnitude contour through this point in Fig. 4.2 is unity, and the marking on the angle contour is y, so that

$$e^{\mathbf{s}} = 1 \angle y. \tag{4.9}$$

In other words, when **s** is a vector of length y in the positive quadrature direction, $e^{\mathbf{s}}$ is a vector of length unity making a counterclockwise angle y with the reference direction. The way in which this comes about may be seen from Fig. 4.4, which

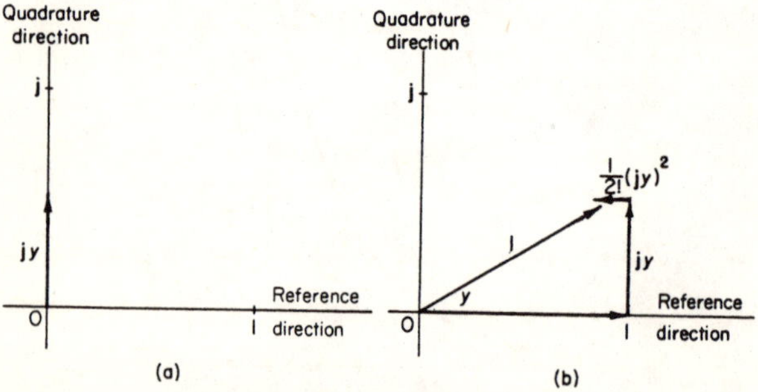

FIG. 4.4. Illustrating formulation of the vector $e^{\mathbf{s}}$ from the series in Eq. (4.5) when $\mathbf{s} = \mathrm{j}y$.

shows what Fig. 4.1 becomes when **s** is given by Eq. (4.8). The vector addition represented by the series on the right-hand side of Eq. (4.5) now leads to the rectangular spiral shown in Fig. 4.4(b). The resultant vector is always of length unity; the counterclockwise angle of the resultant vector, measured in radians, has the value y chosen in Fig. 4.4(a). This is the result expressed by Eqs. (4.8) and (4.9), and we wish to establish this result analytically.

To prove analytically the result expressed by Eqs. (4.8) and (4.9), we substitute from Eq. (4.8) into Eq. (4.5) thereby obtaining

$$e^{\mathbf{j}y} = 1 + (\mathbf{j}y) + \frac{1}{2!}(\mathbf{j}y)^2 + \frac{1}{3!}(\mathbf{j}y)^3 + \cdots. \tag{4.10}$$

In the series on the right-hand side of Eq. (4.10), the odd-numbered terms are represented in Fig. 4.4(b) by the vectors parallel to the reference axis, while the even-numbered terms are represented by the vectors parallel to the quadrature axis. If we replace $\mathbf{j}^2$ by -1 in accordance with the contracted notation introduced in Section 1.6, we may rewrite Eq. (4.10) as

$$e^{\mathbf{j}y} = \left(1 - \frac{1}{2!}y^2 + \frac{1}{4!}y^4 - \cdots\right) + \mathbf{j}\left(y - \frac{1}{3!}y^3 + \frac{1}{5!}y^5 - \cdots\right). \tag{4.11}$$

The first term in brackets on the right-hand side of Eq. (4.11) then represents the vector addition of the vectors parallel to the reference axis in Fig. 4.4(b), while the second term in brackets represents the vector addition of the vectors parallel to the quadrature axis. Now these two expressions in brackets in Eq. (4.11) are in fact the series expansions for cos y and sin y, respectively. Equation (4.11) therefore becomes

$$e^{\mathbf{j}y} = \cos y + \mathbf{j} \sin y. \tag{4.12}$$

Since cos y and sin y are the reference and quadrature components of a unit vector at counterclockwise angle y with the reference direction, Eq. (4.12) may be written

$$e^{\mathbf{j}y} = 1 \angle y \tag{4.13}$$

and this establishes analytically the result expressed by Eqs. (4.8) and (4.9).

The result may be expressed in the form

$$1 \angle y = \cos y + \mathrm{j} \sin y = e^{\mathrm{j}y}. \tag{4.14}$$

These relations state that a unit vector making a counterclockwise angle y with the reference direction has a reference component $\cos y$ and a quadrature component $\sin y$, and the vector may be expressed in terms of the exponential function as $e^{\mathrm{j}y}$.

4.4. Relation between the Exponential Function and the Circular Functions

It should be noted that Eq. (4.12) constitutes a vector relation between the exponential function and the circular functions. Both sides of Eq. (4.12) represent a unit vector at a counterclockwise angle y with the reference direction as shown in Fig. 4.5. Moreover, by changing the sign of y in Eq. (4.12), we obtain

$$e^{-\mathrm{j}y} = \cos y - \mathrm{j} \sin y \tag{4.15}$$

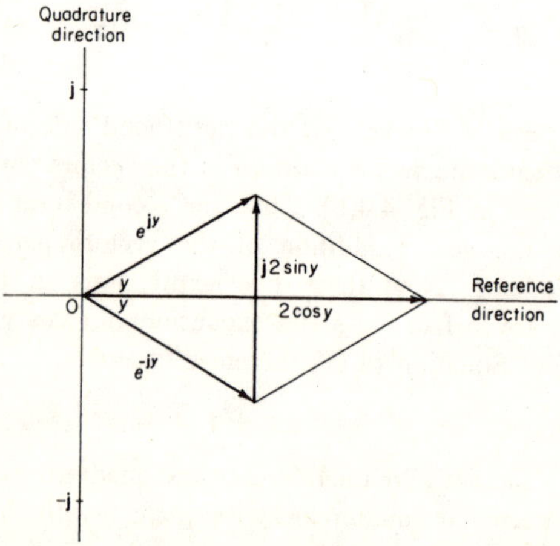

FIG. 4.5. Vector diagram exhibiting the relation between the exponential function and the circular functions.

and both sides of this equation represent a unit vector at a counterclockwise angle $-y$ with the reference direction as shown in Fig. 4.5. Let us now calculate the vectors corresponding to the horizontal and vertical diagonals of the rhombic shown in Fig. 4.5. These diagonal vectors are obtained by adding and subtracting the vectors e^{jy} and e^{-jy} representing the sides of the rhombic through the origin. We therefore add and substract Eqs. (4.12) and (4.15), thereby obtaining

$$e^{jy} + e^{-jy} = 2 \cos y \tag{4.16}$$

$$e^{jy} - e^{-jy} = j2 \sin y. \tag{4.17}$$

These two vector equations express obvious geometrical features of Fig. 4.5. If Eqs. (4.16) and (4.17) are rewritten in the form

$$\cos y = \frac{e^{jy} + e^{-jy}}{2} \tag{4.18}$$

$$\sin y = \frac{e^{jy} - e^{-jy}}{2j} \tag{4.19}$$

they express the circular functions in terms of the exponential function.

4.5. Importance of the Exponential Function for Relating Scalar and Vector Algebra

The representation of a unit vector by means of the exponential function in accordance with Eqs. (4.14) plays a special role in relating vector algebra involving planar products and quotients to scalar algebra. Let **A** be a vector of magnitude A making a counterclockwise angle α with the reference direction, and let **B** be another vector of magnitude B at angle β. Then we may write

$$\mathbf{A} = A \angle\alpha \tag{4.20}$$

$$\mathbf{B} = B \angle\beta \tag{4.21}$$

and it follows that

$$\mathbf{AB} = AB \angle \alpha + \beta \tag{4.22}$$

$$\frac{\mathbf{A}}{\mathbf{B}} = \frac{A}{B} \angle a - \beta. \tag{4.23}$$

Now Eq. (4.14) implies that a unit vector at angle α is represented exponentially by $e^{j\alpha}$, and therefore the vector of magnitude A at angle α in Eq. (4.20) is represented exponentially by $Ae^{j\alpha}$. Similar statements apply to the vectors **B**, **AB**, and **A**/**B** in Eqs. (4.21), (4.22), and (4.23), respectively. Equations (4.20) through (4.23) may therefore be rewritten

$$\mathbf{A} = Ae^{j\alpha} \tag{4.24}$$

$$\mathbf{B} = Be^{j\beta} \tag{4.25}$$

$$\mathbf{AB} = ABe^{j(\alpha+\beta)} \tag{4.26}$$

$$\frac{\mathbf{A}}{\mathbf{B}} = \frac{A}{B}\, e^{j(\alpha-\beta)}. \tag{4.27}$$

Equations (4.24) through (4.27) convey, in terms of the exponential function, the same information as Eqs. (4.20) through (4.23). At first sight it might be thought that Eqs. (4.20) through (4.23) convey the information more simply. However Eqs. (4.24) through (4.27) in fact possess a highly significant advantage. When forming in Eq. (4.22) the planar product of the vectors **A** and **B** given by Eqs. (4.20) and (4.21) we multiply the magnitudes A and B, but we must be extremely careful to add the angles α and β. When this process is carried out with the aid of Eqs. (4.24), (4.25), and (4.26), addition of the angles corresponds to the normal algebraic process of adding indices. Thus, to obtain the exponential factor in Eq. (4.26), we multiply the two exponential factors in Eqs. (4.24) and (4.25), adding the indices in the usual way. In the same way, the exponential factor in Eq. (4.27) is obtained by dividing the exponential factor in Eq. (4.24) by the exponential factor in Eq. (4.25), subtracting the indices in the usual way. We thus see that, by using the exponential representation of a unit vector given in

Eq. (4.14) in the manner shown in Eqs. (4.24) through (4.27), the procedure for forming the planar product of two vectors and the quotient of two vectors merges with the normal procedure for handling indices. For this reason Eqs. (4.20) through (4.23) are in fact more conveniently written with the aid of the exponential function in the form given in Eqs. (4.24) through (4.27).

We thus see that any vector **A** of magnitude A at a counter-clockwise angle α with the reference direction may be written in the form given in Eq. (4.24). Moreover, if this representation is used for all vectors, the rules for forming the planar product and the quotient for two vectors fuse with the process of manipulating the exponential function in the usual way. Thus, the exponential representation of a unit vector given in Eq. (4.14) greatly facilitates the operations of planar multiplication and division of vectors. In fact the procedures involved in these operations have now become identical with the procedures of ordinary algebra.

Moreover, the fuzing of vector algebra using planar products and quotients with scalar algebra in this way extends to the differential and integral calculus. A derivative involves the quotient of two differences, and these operations are subject to vector interpretation. An integral involves the summation of the products of pairs of quantities, and this likewise is subject to vector interpretation. Thus all the usual procedures of the differential and integral calculus, including the procedures for handling differential equations, may be analyzed into the processes of addition, substraction, multiplication, and division and interpreted in vector algebra. This interpretation in vector algebra follows in detail the same rules of procedure as in scalar algebra if the exponential function is used in the manner described by Eqs. (4.24) through (4.27). The ability to convert in this way the whole of scalar algebra and calculus into vector algebra and calculus is what leads mathematicians to refer to vectors in this connection as though they were numbers, and to call the vectors "complex numbers." In oscillation theory, however, we need to avoid confusion between numbers and vectors while at the same time exploiting the fact that the vectors may be handled by means of the same formulas that are used in scalar algebra.

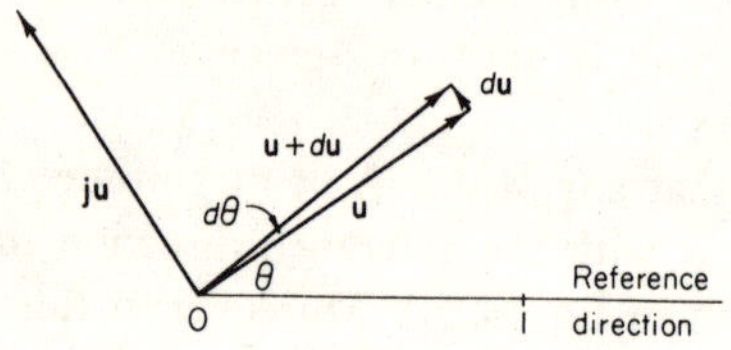

FIG. 4.6. Illustrating the meaning of Eq. (4.24) in terms of rotation of a unit vector **u** from angle θ to angle $\theta + d\theta$.

Let us use Fig. 4.6 to illustrate further how the exponential function permits vector algebra to be handled by the same formulas familiar in scalar algebra. In Fig. 4.6 **u** denotes a vector of unit magnitude at a counterclockwise angle θ with the reference direction. The vector **u** is thus a function of θ, and if for the moment we avoid the use of the exponential function, we may write

$$\mathbf{u}(\theta) = 1 \angle \theta. \tag{4.28}$$

Let us now suppose that the unit vector is rotated counterclockwise through a small angle $d\theta$, so that the vector **u** is replaced by the vector $\mathbf{u} + d\mathbf{u}$ as shown in Fig. 4.6. The vector that must be added to the vector **u** is the small vector $d\mathbf{u}$ indicated in Fig. 4.6. This vector, if sufficiently small, is perpendicular to the vector **u** and is therefore in the direction of the unit vector **ju**. The magnitude of the vector $d\mathbf{u}$ is $d\theta$ since the vectors **u** and $\mathbf{u} + d\mathbf{u}$ are of unit magnitude and there is a small angle $d\theta$ between them. The vector $d\mathbf{u}$ therefore has the direction of the unit vector **ju** and has magnitude $d\theta$, and we may write

$$d\mathbf{u} = \mathbf{ju}\, d\theta. \tag{4.29}$$

Equation (4.29) thus expresses a simple geometrical property of Fig. 4.5. Let us now arrive at Eq. (4.29) using the exponential representation of a unit vector. From Eq. (4.14) it follows that the unit vector at counterclockwise angle θ with the reference direction may be written

$$\mathbf{u}(\theta) = e^{\mathbf{j}\theta}. \tag{4.30}$$

Let us differentiate this equation with respect to θ using in vector algebra the usual rules of differentiation familiar in scalar algebra. We obtain

$$\frac{d\mathbf{u}}{d\theta} = \mathbf{j}e^{\mathbf{j}\theta}. \tag{4.31}$$

If we replace $e^{\mathbf{j}\theta}$ in Eq. (4.31) by $\mathbf{u}$ from Eq. (4.30) we obtain

$$\frac{d\mathbf{u}}{d\theta} = \mathbf{j}\mathbf{u}. \tag{4.32}$$

If this equation is now written in terms of differentials, it becomes Eq. (4.29). Thus, by taking differentials in Eq. (4.30) and applying in vector algebra the rules familiar in scalar algebra, we arrive at Eq. (4.29) which describes the geometrical features of Fig. 4.6.

4.6. Analytical Properties of the Contour Map for the Exponential Function

The cross section along the reference axis of the contour map shown in Fig. 4.2 has been verified analytically in Eq. (4.7) and illustrated graphically in Fig. 4.3. The cross section along the quadrature axis of the contour map in Fig. 4.2 has been verified analytically in Eq. (4.13) and illustrated graphically in Figs. 4.4, 4.5, and 4.6. Let us now establish analytically the remaining properties of the contour map shown in Fig. 4.2.

We are now considering a point P in Fig. 4.2 that is on neither the reference nor the quadrature axis. Let the Cartesian coordinates of the point P be (x, y), so that

$$\mathbf{s} = x + \mathbf{j}y. \tag{4.33}$$

Let us now multiply both sides of Eq. (4.13) by e^x. We thereby obtain

$$e^x e^{jy} = e^x \angle y \tag{4.34}$$

which may be rewritten

$$e^{x+jy} = e^x \angle y. \tag{4.35}$$

On introducing $\mathbf{s}$ from Eq. (4.33), we may express Eq. (4.35) in the form

$$e^{\mathbf{s}} = e^x \angle y. \tag{4.36}$$

It follows that

$$| e^{\mathbf{s}} | = e^x \tag{4.37}$$

and

$$\angle e^{\mathbf{s}} = y. \tag{4.38}$$

Equation (4.37) shows that the magnitude of the vector $e^{\mathbf{s}}$ remains constant along a line $x =$ constant, so that the magnitude contours are parallel to the quadrature axis as shown in Fig. 4.2. Equation (4.38) shows that the angle of the vector $e^{\mathbf{s}}$ remains constant along a line $y =$ constant, so that the angle contours are parallel

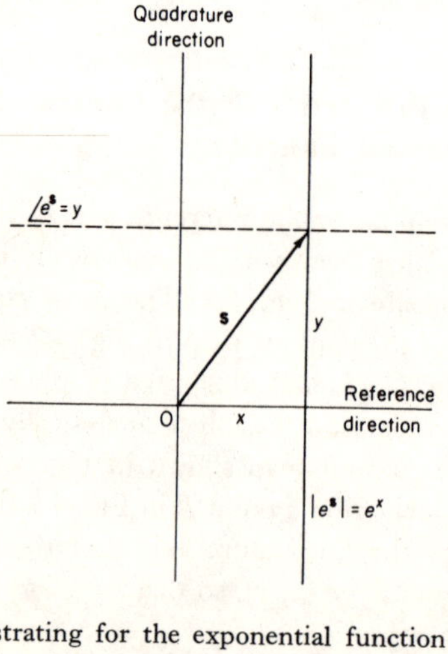

FIG. 4.7. Illustrating for the exponential function the markings on the magnitude and angle contours through the tip of the vector $\mathbf{s} = x + jy$.

to the reference axis as shown in Fig. 4.2. Moreover, Eq. (4.37) shows that the marking on the magnitude contour through the point P in Fig. 4.2 is e^x as shown in Fig. 4.7. It follows that the cross section, along any line parallel to the reference direction, of the terrain associated with the magnitude contours in Figs. 4.2 and 4.7 is given by the graph shown in Fig. 4.3. Likewise Eq. (4.38) shows that the markings on the angle contour through the point P in Fig. 4.2 is y, as shown in Fig. 4.7. Thus the marking on an angle contour is equal to the distance of that contour above the reference axis, so that the angle contours are equally spaced as shown in Fig. 4.2.

4.7. The Concept of Actance

We are now in a position to obtain an analytical representation of the rotating vectors used in handling oscillations. This involves studying the time-varying vector

$$e^{\mathbf{s}t} \tag{4.39}$$

where t denotes time and $\mathbf{s}$ is a vector that does not vary with time and that we shall call the actance of the oscillation.

Study of the vector $e^{\mathbf{s}t}$ involves replacing $\mathbf{s}$ in Fig. 4.2 by $\mathbf{s}t$, as shown in Fig. 4.8. As the time t increases, the vector $\mathbf{s}t$ in Fig. 4.8 lengthens uniformly without changing its direction. The tip of the vector $\mathbf{s}t$ therefore runs along the sloping broken line indicated. From the way in which the tip of the vector $\mathbf{s}t$ crosses the magnitude contours, we may read the way in which the magnitude of the vector $e^{\mathbf{s}t}$ varies with time t. From the way in which the tip of the vector $\mathbf{s}t$ crosses the angle contours we may read the time variation in the angle of the vector $e^{\mathbf{s}t}$. When the direction of the vector $\mathbf{s}$ points into the first quadrant as indicated in Fig. 4.8, we see that the tip of the vector $\mathbf{s}t$ crosses the magnitude contours in such a way as to correspond to an exponential increase in the magnitude of the vector $e^{\mathbf{s}t}$. At the same time the tip of the vector $\mathbf{s}t$ crosses the angle contours in such a way as to correspond to uniform rotation of the vector $e^{\mathbf{s}t}$ in the counterclockwise direction. Thus, with the direction of the actance vector **s** pointing into the first quadrant as indicated in Fig. 4.8, the vector e^{st} spirals as shown in Fig. 4.9(c). When $t = 0$ the vector e^{st} is a unit vector in the reference direction, and as t increases the vector e^{st} executes a counterclockwise increasing spiral as shown in Fig. 4.9(c).

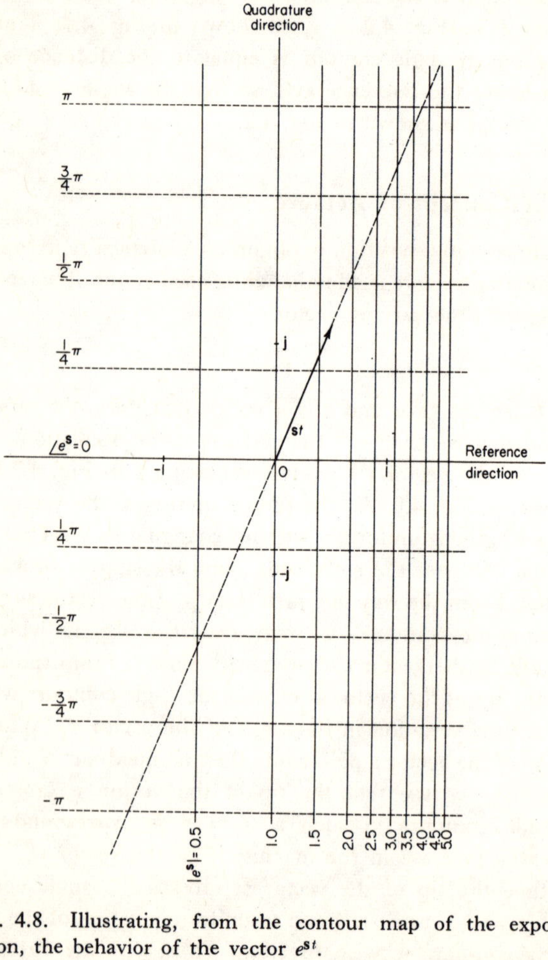

FIG. 4.8. Illustrating, from the contour map of the exponential function, the behavior of the vector e^{st}.

The character of the spiral executed by the vector e^{st} is controlled by the magnitude and direction of the actance vector **s**. If **s** points along the quadrature direction in Fig. 4.8, then the tip of the vector **s***t* runs along the magnitude contour whose marking is unity, while crossing the angle contours at a uniform rate. In these circumstances e^{st} is a unit vector that rotates uniformly in the counterclockwise direction as indicated in Fig. 4.9(b), passing through the reference direction at time zero.

If in Fig. 4.8 the actance **s** points into the second quadrant between the positive quadrature axis and the negative reference

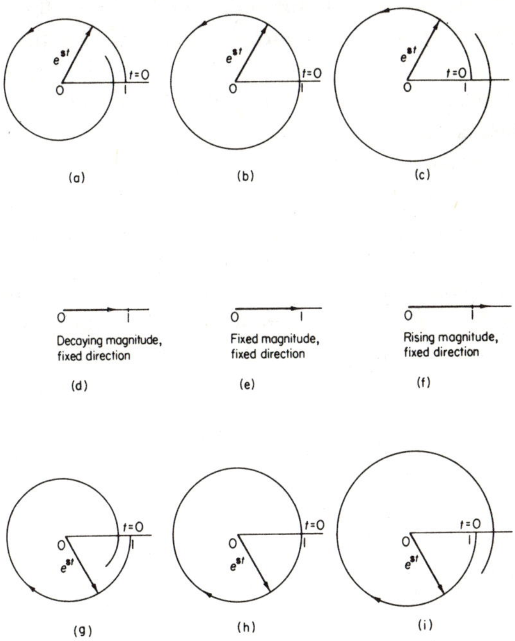

FIG. 4.9. Illustrating the time variation of the vector e^{st} when the tip of the actance vector **s** is (a) in the second quadrant, (b) on the positive quadrature axis, (c) in the first quadrant, (d) on the negative reference axis, (e) at the origin, (f) on the positive reference axis, (g) in the third quadrant, (h) on the negative quadrature axis, and (i) in the fourth quadrant.

axis, so also does the vector $\mathbf{s}t$ for positive values of t. With lapse of time, the tip of the vector $\mathbf{s}t$ then crosses the magnitude contours in such a way as to cause an exponential decrease with time in the magnitude of the vector $e^{\mathbf{s}t}$. At the same time the tip of the vector $\mathbf{s}t$ crosses the angle contours in such a way as to cause uniform counterclockwise rotation of the vector $e^{\mathbf{s}t}$. Thus, when the actance $\mathbf{s}$ points into the second quadrant in Fig. 4.8, the vector $e^{\mathbf{s}t}$ executes the counterclockwise decreasing spiral indicated in Fig. 4.9(a).

If the direction of the actance $\mathbf{s}$ points below the reference axis in Fig. 4.8 so that the quadrature component of $\mathbf{s}$ is negative, then, with increasing time, the tip of the vector $\mathbf{s}t$ moves downwards across the angle contours. This means that the counterclockwise angle made by the vector $e^{\mathbf{s}t}$ with the reference direction in decreasing uniformly with lapse of time. Thus, when the actance $\mathbf{s}$ has a negative quadrature component, the vector $e^{\mathbf{s}t}$ rotates clockwise instead of counterclockwise, as shown in Fig. 4.9(g, h, and i).

If the actance $\mathbf{s}$ lies along the reference axis in Fig. 4.8, so also does the vector $\mathbf{s}t$. The tip of the vector $\mathbf{s}t$ then runs along the reference axis with lapse of time. It is therefore running along the angle contour whose marking is zero, so that the vector $e^{\mathbf{s}t}$ maintains a zero angle with the reference direction. However, the magnitude of the vector $e^{\mathbf{s}t}$ varies exponentially with time, increasing if the vector $\mathbf{s}$ points along the positive reference direction, and decreasing if the vector $\mathbf{s}$ points along the negative reference direction. In Fig. 4.9 the increasing exponential function is indicated in diagram (f) while the decreasing exponential function is indicated in diagram (d). Figure 4.9(e) illustrates the special case for which $\mathbf{s} = 0$, when the vector $e^{\mathbf{s}t}$ is a unit vector in the reference direction and does not vary with time.

From Fig. 4.9 we see that $e^{\mathbf{s}t}$ is a time-varying vector the tip of which in general executes a spiral. Depending upon the magnitude and direction of the actance $\mathbf{s}$, the spiral may either increase or decrease exponentially, and may involve uniform rotation in either the counterclockwise or clockwise directions.

Important degenerate cases also occur. In one of these the vector e^{st} does not rotate at all, but its magnitude increases or decreases exponentially. Another important degenerate case is the one in which the vector e^{st} spirals neither outwards nor inwards; it maintains a constant magnitude of unity but rotates either in the counterclockwise direction or clockwise direction. This is the case for which the reference component of the time-varying vector e^{st} represents a sinusoidal oscillation of constant amplitude.

The way in which the magnitude and angle of the actance **s** controls the spiral executed by the vector e^{st} may be described analytically as follows: Let

$$\mathbf{f}(t) = e^{st} \tag{4.40}$$

so that

$$\frac{d\mathbf{f}}{dt} = \mathbf{s}e^{st}. \tag{4.41}$$

By dividing Eq. (4.41) by Eq. (4.40) and transposing, we obtain

$$\mathbf{s} = \frac{1}{\mathbf{f}}\frac{d\mathbf{f}}{dt}. \tag{4.42}$$

In Fig. 4.10 is shown the vector **f** given by Eq. (4.40) both at

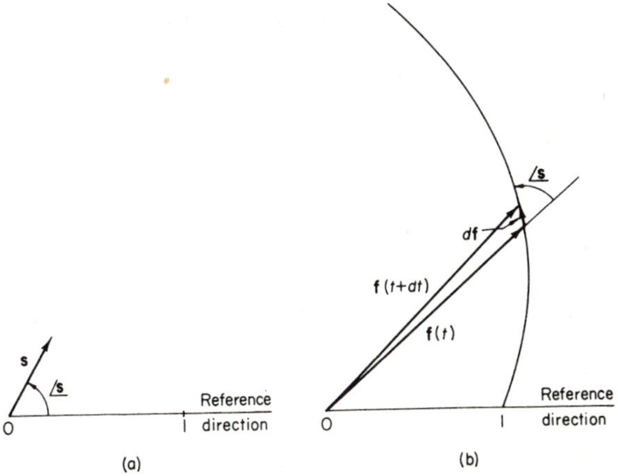

FIG. 4.10. Illustrating the fact that the tip of the vector e^{st} executes an equiangular spiral of angle $\angle\mathbf{s}$.

time t and at a slightly later time $t + dt$. The vector excess of the latter vector over the former is the small vector $d\mathbf{f}$ shown. The relation between the vectors **s**, **f**, and $d\mathbf{f}$ is described by Eq. (4.42). We deduce from Eq. (4.42) that

$$|\mathbf{s}| = \frac{1}{|\mathbf{f}|}\frac{|d\mathbf{f}|}{dt} \tag{4.43}$$

and

$$\angle\mathbf{s} = \angle d\mathbf{f} - \angle\mathbf{f}. \tag{4.44}$$

Equation (4.44) shows that the angle between the vector $d\mathbf{f}$ in Fig. 4.10 and the vector $\mathbf{f}(t)$ is constant and equal to $\angle\mathbf{s}$. In other words the spiral executed by the vector $e^{\mathbf{s}t}$ maintains a constant angle between the tangent and the radius vector, and this angle is equal to $\angle\mathbf{s}$. The spiral executed by $e^{\mathbf{s}t}$ is thus what is known as an equiangular spiral of angle $\angle\mathbf{s}$. The equiangular spiral shown in Fig. 4.9(c) has an angle between zero and $\frac{1}{2}\pi$. The equiangular spiral shown in Fig. 4.9(a) has an angle between $\frac{1}{2}\pi$ and π. The equiangular spirals shown in Fig. 4.9(g and i) have negative angles. Figure 4.9(f) represents a degenerate equiangular spiral of zero angle, while Fig. 4.9(d) represents a degenerate equiangular spiral of angle π. Figure 4.9(b) represents a degenerate equiangular spiral of angle $\frac{1}{2}\pi$, while Fig. 4.9(h) represents a degenerate equiangular spiral of angle $-\frac{1}{2}\pi$. Thus, from the angle of the actance vector **s** we may picture the type of equiangular spiral described by the vector $e^{\mathbf{s}t}$.

Particular importance attaches to the reference and quadrature components of the actance **s**. Let these be denoted by σ and ω, respectively, so that

$$\mathbf{s} = \sigma + \mathbf{j}\omega. \tag{4.45}$$

We then have

$$\mathbf{s}t = \sigma t + \mathbf{j}\omega t \tag{4.46}$$

and it follows from Eq. (4.36) that

$$e^{\mathbf{s}t} = e^{\sigma t} \angle\omega t. \tag{4.47}$$

This equation conveys the information that

$$| e^{st} | = e^{\sigma t} \tag{4.48}$$

and

$$\angle e^{st} = \omega t. \tag{4.49}$$

Equation (4.48) states that the magnitude of the vector e^{st} is increasing exponentially at the rate σ nepers per unit time. Equation (4.49) states that the counterclockwise angle made by the vector e^{st} with the reference direction is increasing uniformly at the rate ω radians per unit time. In other words the vector e^{st} increases in magnitude exponentially at the rate σ nepers per unit time while rotating in the counterclockwise direction uniformly with angular velocity ω. This is the behavior indicated in Fig. 4.9(c). We thus see that the reference component of the actance vector $\mathbf{s}$ gives the rate of increase of the magnitude of the vector e^{st} measured in nepers per unit time, while the quadrature component of the actance vector $\mathbf{s}$ gives the rate of counterclockwise rotation of the vector e^{st} in radians per unit time. If σ is negative the magnitude of the vector e^{st} decreases as shown in Fig. 4.9(a). If ω is negative, the vector e^{st} rotates in the clockwise direction as shown in Fig. 4.9(i). If both σ and ω are negative, the vector e^{st} executes a decreasing spiral in the clockwise direction as shown in Fig. 4.9(g).

If ω vanishes, the vector e^{st} does not rotate and reduces to the scalar exponential time function. If σ vanishes, there is no variation in the magnitude of the vector e^{st}, which then rotates uniformly with angular velocity ω in the counterclockwise direction as shown in Fig. 4.9(b); if ω is negative the rotation is clockwise as shown in Fig. 4.9(h). Particular importance attaches to the case when σ vanishes. Equation (4.45) then becomes

$$\mathbf{s} = \mathbf{j}\omega \tag{4.50}$$

so that Eq. (4.47) becomes

$$e^{\mathbf{j}\omega t} = 1 \angle \omega t. \tag{4.51}$$

Equation (4.51) is what Eq. (4.13) becomes when y is replaced by ωt. It follows from Eq. (4.51) that $e^{j\omega t}$ is a unit vector that points in the reference direction at time zero and that rotates in the counterclockwise direction with uniform angular velocity ω; if ω is numerically negative, the rotation is in the clockwise direction. Tremendous importance attaches to the representation of a unit vector rotating with uniform angular velocity ω by means of the exponential function in the manner described by Eq. (4.51).

In analyzing the behavior of a linear oscillatory system, a function of time is frequently represented as the reference component of a time-varying vector. Figure 4.9 illustrates a number of time-varying vectors of great practical importance. The reference component of the time-varying vector illustrated in Fig. 4.9(b) or Fig. 4.9(h) constitutes a sinusoidal oscillation of constant amplitude. The reference component of the time-varying vector illustrated in Fig. 4.9(c) or Fig. 4.9(i) constitutes an oscillation the amplitude of which increases exponentially with time. The reference component of the time-varying vector shown in Fig. 4.9(a) or Fig. 4.9(g) represents an oscillation the amplitude of which decreases exponentially with time. These are all time functions of great importance in the study of oscillations, and they are most conveniently represented as the reference components of the time-varying vectors illustrated in Fig. 4.9 and represented analytically by e^{st} for appropriate magnitudes and directions of the actance **s**.

4.8. The Actance Diagram

In the previous section we have described the relation between the time-varying vector e^{st} and the actance vector **s**. This relation is conveniently summarized in the actance diagram shown in Fig. 4.11. Figure 4.11 illustrates the plane of the actance vector **s**, whose reference component is σ and whose quadrature component is ω. When the tip of the actance vector is in the first, second, third, and fourth quadrants of the actance diagram, the vector e^{st} spirals in the manner shown in Fig. 4.9(c, a, g, and i), respectively. When the actance vector points along the positive quadrature axis in Fig. 4.11, the tip of the vector e^{st} describes a circle with uniform angular velocity ω in the counterclockwise direction as shown in Fig. 4.9(b), and the reference component of the vector executes a sinusoidal oscillation of angular frequency ω and constant amplitude. The positive quadrature axis in an

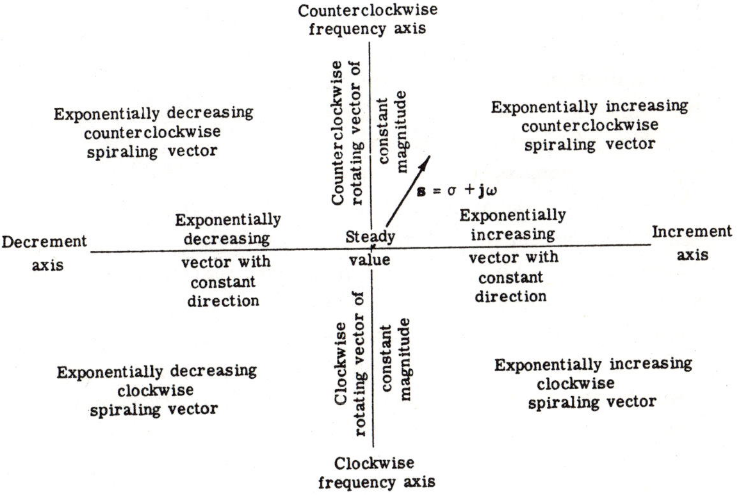

FIG. 4.11. An actance diagram illustrating, for different directions of the actance vector **s**, the character of the time-varying vector e^{st}; compare Fig. 4.9.

actance diagram is therefore conveniently labeled the counterclockwise frequency axis. When the actance vector **s** points along the negative quadrature axis in Fig. 4.11, the tip of the vector e^{st} executes a circular motion with uniform angular velocity ω in the clockwise direction as shown in Fig. 4.9(h), and the reference component of the vector executes a sinusoidal oscillation of angular frequency ω and constant amplitude. The negative quadrature axis in an actance diagram is therefore conveniently labeled the clockwise frequency axis. When the actance vector **s** points in the positive reference direction in Fig. 4.11, the vector e^{st} points steadily in the reference direction but increases in magnitude exponentially with time. The positive reference axis in an actance diagram is therefore conveniently labeled the increment axis. When the actance vector **s** points along the negative reference direction in Fig. 4.11, the vector e^{st} again points steadily in the reference direction, but its magnitude decreases exponentially with time. The negative reference axis in an actance diagram is therefore conveniently labeled the decrement axis.

The diagrams in Fig. 4.9 have been drawn so as to indicate the behavior of the vector e^{st} for the various directions of the vector **s** in the actance diagram of Fig. 4.11. Figures 4.9(a, c, g, and i) correspond to the four quadrants. Figure 4.9(b, d, f, and h) correspond to the axes, while Fig. 4.9(e) corresponds to the origin in the actance diagram. In each case the increment component σ of the actance vector **s** gives the rate of increase in the magnitude of the vector e^{st} in nepers per unit time. If **s** has a decrement component rather than an increment component, then the magnitude of the vector e^{st} decreases exponentially rather than increases. The counterclockwise frequency component ω of the actance vector **s** gives the angular velocity of the vector e^{st} in the counterclockwise direction. If **s** has a clockwise frequency component rather than a counterclockwise frequency component, then the vector e^{st} rotates in the clockwise direction rather than the counterclockwise direction.

The time variations executed by the reference component of the vector e^{st} for different positions of the tip of the vector **s** in the actance diagram incorporate some of the most important time variations involved in oscillation theory. The origin in the actance diagram corresponds to the steady values encountered, for example, in steady motion or in direct-current electric circuits. Points on the frequency axis correspond to sinusoidal oscillations of constant amplitude. Points off the frequency axis correspond to oscillations whose amplitudes vary exponentially with time, decreasing on the decrement side of the frequency axis and increasing on the increment side. In using a point on the counterclockwise side of the increment and decrement axes we are representing the oscillation as the reference component of a vector that rotates in the counterclockwise direction. If we use the mirror image of the point in the increment and decrement axes, we are adopting the alternative representation of the oscillation as the reference component of a vector that rotates in the clockwise direction. The increment axis itself corresponds to a situation where there is no oscillation but simply an exponential increase of magnitude with time, while the decrement axis corresponds to a situation involving no oscillation but simply an exponential decrease of magnitude with time.

4.9. The Concept of Vector Amplitude

In the preceding two sections we have seen that an oscillation may be represented as the reference component of a spiraling vector. The magnitude of the spiraling vector at time t is known as the amplitude of the oscillation at time t. The counterclockwise angle that the spiraling vector makes with the reference direction at time zero is known as the phase of the oscillation. From Fig. 4.9 we see that, at time zero, the spiraling vector e^{st} is a unit vector in the reference direction. The reference component of the spiraling vector e^{st} therefore represents an oscillation of zero phase with unit amplitude at time zero. We need to be able to represent in this way oscillations of nonzero phase having an amplitude at time zero differing from unity. For this purpose it is convenient to introduce the concept of vector amplitude.

Let us suppose that the oscillation under consideration has a phase α and that the amplitude at time zero is V_0. If the oscillation is represented as the reference component of a counterclockwise spiraling vector, this vector must, at time zero, have magnitude V_0 and make a counterclockwise angle α with the reference direction. It is therefore convenient to introduce the fixed vector

$$\mathbf{V}_0 = V_0 \angle\alpha \tag{4.52}$$

and then to consider the spiraling vector

$$\mathbf{V}(t) = \mathbf{V}_0 e^{\mathbf{s}t}. \tag{4.53}$$

If Eq. (4.52) is expressed with the aid of the exponential function, we obtain

$$\mathbf{V}_0 = V_0 e^{\mathrm{j}\alpha}. \tag{4.54}$$

If we now substitute into Eq. (4.53) for $\mathbf{V}_0$ from Eq. (4.54) and for $\mathbf{s}$ from Eq. (4.45), we obtain

$$\mathbf{V}(t) = V_0 e^{\mathrm{j}\alpha} e^{(\sigma+\mathrm{j}\omega)t}. \tag{4.55}$$

This equation may be rearranged as

$$\mathbf{V}(t) = V_0 e^{\sigma t} e^{\mathrm{j}(\omega t+\alpha)}. \tag{4.56}$$

We therefore see that the time-varying vector $\mathbf{V}(t)$ has, at time t, a magnitude

$$V_0 e^{\sigma t} \tag{4.57}$$

and makes with the reference direction a counterclockwise angle

$$\omega t + \alpha. \tag{4.58}$$

The reference component of the vector $\mathbf{V}(t)$ is therefore

$$v(t) = V_0 e^{\sigma t} \cos(\omega t + \alpha). \tag{4.59}$$

Equation (4.59) represents an oscillation of angular frequency ω and phase α; the amplitude is V_0 at time zero, and the amplitude increases with time at the rate σ nepers per unit time. We thus see that, to represent vectorially the oscillation given by Eq. (4.59), we proceed as follows: First we combine σ and ω to form the actance vector

$$\mathbf{s} = \sigma + \mathrm{j}\omega. \tag{4.60}$$

Then we combine V_0 and α to form the vector amplitude

$$\mathbf{V}_0 = V_0 \angle\alpha. \tag{4.61}$$

In terms of the vector actance and vector amplitude thus defined, the oscillation given by Eq. (4.59) is the reference component of the spiraling vector

$$\mathbf{V}(t) = \mathbf{V}_0 e^{\mathbf{s}t} \tag{4.62}$$

and may be described as an oscillation of actance **s** given by Eq. (4.60) and vector amplitude $\mathbf{V}_0$ given by Eq. (4.61). The spiral representing the vector $\mathbf{V}(t)$ in Eq. (4.62) is obtained by rotating the spiral representing e^{st} through the counterclockwise angle α and multiplying the scale by V_0 in accordance with Eq. (4.61).

If the oscillation under consideration is a sinusoidal oscillation of constant amplitude, then σ vanishes, and Eqs. (4.59) and (4.60) become

$$v(t) = V_0 \cos(\omega t + \alpha) \tag{4.63}$$

and

$$\mathbf{s} = \mathbf{j}\omega \tag{4.64}$$

so that Eq. (4.62) may be written

$$\mathbf{V}(t) = \mathbf{V}_0 e^{\mathbf{j}\omega t}. \tag{4.65}$$

The tip of the time-varying vector represented by Eq. (4.65) executes a circular motion in the counterclockwise direction with uniform angular velocity ω, and the vector coincides at time zero with the vector $\mathbf{V}_0$ given by Eq. (4.61). The reference component of the rotating vector $\mathbf{V}(t)$ in Eq. (4.65) executes the sinusoidal oscillation of constant amplitude given in Eq. (4.63).

We may summarize as follows. Let us suppose that we have an oscillation of angular frequency ω and phase α. Let the amplitude at time zero be V_0 and let the amplitude increase exponentially with time at the rate σ nepers per unit time. This is the oscillation

$$v(t) = V_0 e^{\sigma t} \cos(\omega t + \alpha). \tag{4.66}$$

We introduce an actance vector defined by

$$\mathbf{s} = \sigma + \mathbf{j}\omega \tag{4.67}$$

and an amplitude vector defined by

$$\mathbf{V}_0 = V_0 \angle\alpha = V_0 e^{\mathbf{j}\alpha} \tag{4.68}$$

and then consider the spiraling vector

$$\mathbf{V}(t) = \mathbf{V}_0 e^{st}. \tag{4.69}$$

The reference component of this spiraling vector is the oscillation given by Eq. (4.66), which may therefore be described as an oscillation of actance $\mathbf{s}$ given by Eq. (4.67) and vector amplitude $\mathbf{V}_0$ given by Eq. (4.68). The spiral representing the vector $\mathbf{V}(t)$ in Eq. (4.69) is obtained by rotating the spiral representing e^{st} through the counterclockwise angle α and multiplying the scale by V_0 in accordance with Eq. (4.68).

4.10. The Concepts of Complex Amplitude and Complex Frequency

As explained in connection with the table on page 21, the algebra of complex numbers is identical with the vector algebra that we have developed and used. In the notation of complex numbers, however, it is customary to drop the vector symbolism without dropping the vector significance. Furthermore, in the language of complex numbers, what we have called in the previous section the vector amplitude is known as the "complex amplitude," while what we have called the actance in Section 4.7 is known as the "complex angular frequency." Thus, in the language of complex numbers, the oscillation given by Eq. (4.59) is described as an oscillation of complex angular frequency $\sigma + j\omega$ and complex amplitude $V_0 e^{j\alpha}$. The oscillation is the "real part" of the spiraling "complex number" given by Eq. (4.55) or Eq. (4.56) customarily written without the vector symbolism.

It should be mentioned that, while complex angular frequency is the name commonly given to $s = \sigma + j\omega$ in electric system theory, it is more usual in electro-magnetic theory to call $\omega - j\sigma$ $(= -js)$ the complex angular frequency, so that the real part of the complex frequency is the actual frequency. The latter would seem to be the preferable practice and could be adopted universally if the name "actance" were used for s as in Sections 4.7, 4.8, and 4.9 of this book.

Summarizing Exercises

4.1. With the aid of vector diagrams explain what is meant by the exponential function of a vector **s**. Discuss the particular case when **s** is a vector of length y pointing in the quadrature direction.

4.2. Justify the formulas

$$\cos y = \frac{e^{\mathrm{j}y} + e^{-\mathrm{j}y}}{2}$$

$$\sin y = \frac{e^{\mathrm{j}y} - e^{-\mathrm{j}y}}{2\mathrm{j}}$$

and illustrate them in a vector diagram.

4.3. Show that, if $\mathbf{s} = x + \mathrm{j}y$, then $e^{\mathbf{s}} = e^{x} \angle y$. Draw a contour map in the **s** plane for the magnitude and angle of the vector $e^{\mathbf{s}}$.

4.4. For the contour map in the previous exercise, show that the cross section along the reference axis gives the graph of the scalar exponential function. Show that the cross section along the quadrature axis gives a vector of unit magnitude with variable direction. Explain how the counterclockwise angle of the unit vector varies with position along the quadrature axis.

4.5. Explain why a vector **A** of magnitude A at a counterclockwise angle α with the reference direction may be written

$$\mathbf{A} = Ae^{\mathrm{j}\alpha}.$$

Explain further why, with this mode of representation, the operations of planar product and quotient of vectors merge with the normal procedure for handling indices when multiplying and dividing exponential functions. Describe how the exponential function permits vector algebra involving planar products and quotients to be handled by the same formulas familiar in scalar algebra.

4.6. If $\mathbf{u}(\theta) = e^{\mathbf{j}\theta}$, deduce that $d\mathbf{u} = \mathbf{j}\mathbf{u}\, d\theta$ and explain the meaning of this relation in a vector diagram.

4.7. If ω is an angular velocity and t denotes time, show that $e^{\mathbf{j}\omega t}$ is a vector of unit magnitude that rotates in the counterclockwise direction with uniform angular velocity ω and passes through the reference direction at time zero.

4.8. Using the contour map of the exponential function, illustrate how the time variation of the magnitude and direction of the vector $e^{\mathbf{s}t}$, where t denotes time, depends on the magnitude and direction of the vector **s**. Illustrate with vector diagrams the time variation of $e^{\mathbf{s}t}$ when the tip of the vector **s** is (a) in the first quadrant of the **s** plane, (b) in the second quadrant, (c) in the third quadrant, (d) in the fourth quadrant, (e) on the positive reference axis, (f) on the negative reference axis, (g) on the positive quadrature axis, (h) on the negative quadrature axis, and (i) at the origin.

4.9. Explain what is meant by vector actance. Show that the reference component of the actance vector **s** gives the rate of increase of the magnitude of the vector $e^{\mathbf{s}t}$, where t denotes time, while the quadrature component of **s** gives the counterclockwise angular velocity of $e^{\mathbf{s}t}$.

4.10. Explain what is meant by an actance diagram. Explain how the axes are labeled and why. Draw an actance diagram, and indicate for the various axes and quadrants the behavior of the vector $e^{\mathbf{s}t}$, where **s** denotes actance and t denotes time.

4.11. Explain what is meant by an equiangular spiral. Show that, if t denotes time, the tip of the vector $\mathbf{f}(t) = e^{\mathbf{s}t}$ describes an equiangular spiral whose angle is $\angle\mathbf{s}$. Show also that

$$|\mathbf{s}| = \frac{1}{|\mathbf{f}|}\frac{|d\mathbf{f}|}{dt}.$$

4.12. If $\mathbf{s} = \sigma + \mathbf{j}\omega$ and t denotes time, show that the reference component of the vector $e^{\mathbf{s}t}$ is a sinusoidal oscillation of angular frequency ω radians per unit time whose amplitude increases at the rate σ nepers per unit time. Show also that the phase of the oscillation is zero and that the amplitude at time zero is unity.

4.13. Explain what is meant by the vector amplitude of an oscillation. An oscillation has angular frequency ω and phase α. At time zero the oscillation has amplitude A, and the amplitude is increasing exponentially at the rate σ nepers per unit time. If t denotes time, show that the oscillation is the reference component of the vector $\mathbf{A}e^{\mathbf{s}t}$ where $\mathbf{A} = Ae^{\mathbf{j}\alpha}$ and $\mathbf{s} = \sigma + \mathbf{j}\omega$.

4.14. Restate the results in Exercise 4.13 using the language and notation of complex numbers, and in particular using the concepts of complex amplitude and complex angular frequency.

PROBLEMS

1. The Technique of Handling Oscillations

1.1. If $\mathbf{s}_1$ and $\mathbf{s}_2$ are a pair of given vectors, illustrate graphically the vectors represented by $\frac{1}{2}(\mathbf{s}_1 + \mathbf{s}_2)$ and $\frac{1}{2}(\mathbf{s}_1 - \mathbf{s}_2)$.

1.2. If the tips of the vectors $\mathbf{s}_1$, $\mathbf{s}_2$, and $\mathbf{s}_3$ are the vertices of a triangle, find the position vector of the centroid of the triangle.

1.3. Prove that the planar product of **A** with **B** is identical with the planar product of **B** with **A**.

1.4. If $\mathbf{C} = \mathbf{AB}$ show that the reference component of **C** is not in general equal to the product of the reference component of **A** and the reference component of **B**.

1.5. Show that $(a + jb)(a - jb) = a^2 + b^2$.

1.6. Show that

$$\frac{1}{a + jb} = \frac{a - jb}{a^2 + b^2}.$$

1.7. Show that the reference component of the reciprocal of a vector is not in general equal to the reciprocal of the reference component of the vector.

1.8. Explain what is meant by the statement that any positive scalar quantity *a* may be regarded as a vector of magnitude *a* pointing in the reference direction. State how a negative scalar quantity may be regarded as a vector.

1.9. Find the reference and quadrature components of the vectors:

$$1 \angle \frac{\pi}{3}, \quad 4 \angle \frac{3\pi}{4}, \quad 2 \angle \frac{7\pi}{6}, \quad 3 \angle -\frac{5\pi}{6}, \quad 5 \angle -\frac{\pi}{3}, \quad 6 \angle \frac{13\pi}{6}.$$

1.10. Find the reference and quadrature components of the vectors:

$$\frac{1}{1-j}, \quad \frac{1-j}{1+j}, \quad \frac{1-j}{(1+j)^2}, \quad \frac{(1-j)^2}{1+j}, \quad (1+j)^2, \quad (1-j)^3.$$

1.11. Find the magnitudes and directions of the vectors:

$$1+j\sqrt{3}, \quad \frac{1}{1-j\sqrt{3}}, \quad (1-j\sqrt{3})^2, \quad \frac{1}{(\sqrt{3}+j)^2},$$
$$(\sqrt{3}-j)^2, \quad (\sqrt{3}+j)^3.$$

1.12. Calculate $\sqrt{\mathbf{A}}$ when $\mathbf{A}$ is equal to:

$$1+j, \quad 1+j\sqrt{3}, \quad \frac{1}{1-j\sqrt{3}}.$$

In each case ascertain all possible values of $\sqrt{\mathbf{A}}$.

1.13. Find the magnitudes and directions of the vectors formed by taking the reciprocals of the vectors:

$$1+j\sqrt{3}, \quad \frac{1-j}{1+j}, \quad (1-j\sqrt{3})^2, \quad (\sqrt{3}+j)^2, \quad (\sqrt{3}-j)^2,$$
$$(\sqrt{3}+j)^3.$$

1.14. Find the reference and quadrature components of the vectors formed by taking the mirror images in the reference axis of the vectors:

$$1+j, \quad -1-j, \quad 1+j\sqrt{3}, \quad -1+j\sqrt{3}, \quad \frac{1}{1-j\sqrt{3}}, \quad \frac{(1-j)^2}{1+j}.$$

1.15 Find the magnitudes and directions of the vectors formed by taking the mirror images in the reference axis of the vectors:

$$\frac{1}{1-j}, \quad \frac{1-j}{1+j}, \quad \frac{1+j}{(1-j)^2}, \quad (1-j\sqrt{3})^2, \quad (1+j)^3, \quad (\sqrt{3}-j)^3.$$

1.16. If $\mathbf{A} = A \angle \alpha$ and $\mathbf{A}^*$ is the mirror image of $\mathbf{A}$ in the reference axis, find in terms of A and α the magnitudes and directions of the vectors:

$$\mathbf{A}+\mathbf{A}^*, \quad \mathbf{A}-\mathbf{A}^*, \quad \mathbf{A}\mathbf{A}^*, \quad \mathbf{A}/\mathbf{A}^*.$$

1.17. If an asterisk appended to a vector implies that the mirror image of the vector is to be taken in the reference axis, prove that:

(i) If $\mathbf{A}+\mathbf{B}=\mathbf{C}$, then $\mathbf{A}^*+\mathbf{B}^*=\mathbf{C}^*$.
(ii) If $\mathbf{A}\mathbf{B}=\mathbf{C}$, then $\mathbf{A}^*\mathbf{B}^*=\mathbf{C}^*$.
(iii) If $\mathbf{A}/\mathbf{B}=\mathbf{C}$, then $\mathbf{A}^*/\mathbf{B}^*=\mathbf{C}^*$.

1.18. Find the magnitudes and directions of the vectors obtained by taking the square roots of the following vectors:

$$4\angle\frac{\pi}{6},\quad 1\angle\frac{3\pi}{4},\quad 16\angle\frac{4\pi}{3},\quad 9\angle\frac{2\pi}{5},\quad 25\angle\frac{7\pi}{3},\quad \frac{9}{4}\angle-\frac{\pi}{5}.$$

1.19. Find the reference and quadrature components of the vectors obtained by taking the square roots of the following vectors:

$$\frac{1}{16}\angle-\pi,\quad \frac{16}{9}\angle\frac{4\pi}{3},\quad \frac{9}{25}\angle-\frac{2\pi}{3},\quad \frac{25}{4}\angle\frac{\pi}{3},\quad \frac{4}{9}\angle-\frac{4\pi}{3},$$
$$\frac{1}{25}\angle-\frac{\pi}{2}.$$

1.20. Find the magnitudes and directions of the vectors obtained by taking the square roots of the following vectors:

$$9\mathbf{j},\quad -4\mathbf{j},\quad \tfrac{1}{2}(1+\mathbf{j}\sqrt{3}),\quad 18(1+\mathbf{j}\sqrt{3}),\quad -8(1-\mathbf{j}\sqrt{3}),$$
$$-\frac{25}{2}(1+\mathbf{j}\sqrt{3}).$$

1.21. Find the reference and quadrature components of the vectors obtained by taking the square roots of the vectors:

$$16\mathbf{j},\quad -36,\quad \tfrac{1}{2}(1-\mathbf{j}\sqrt{3}),\quad -2(1+\mathbf{j}\sqrt{3}),\quad \tfrac{9}{2}(1+\mathbf{j}\sqrt{3}),$$
$$-\tfrac{25}{2}(1-\mathbf{j}\sqrt{3}).$$

1.22. Find all the vectors $\mathbf{s}$ satisfying (a) the equation $\mathbf{s}^2 + 1 = 0$, and (b) the equation $\mathbf{s}^2 - 1 = 0$.

1.23. If $\boldsymbol{\omega} = 1\angle 2\pi/3$, calculate the magnitudes and directions of the vectors $\boldsymbol{\omega}^2$ and $\boldsymbol{\omega}^3$. Deduce the three vectors obtained by taking the cube root of a unit vector in the reference direction. Prove that:

$$1 + \boldsymbol{\omega} + \boldsymbol{\omega}^2 = 0.$$

1.24. Find all vectors $\mathbf{s}$ satisfying the equation $\mathbf{s}^3 + 1 = 0$.

1.25. Find all vectors $\mathbf{s}$ satisfying the equation $\mathbf{s}^4 - 1 = 0$.

1.26. Find all the vectors $\mathbf{s}$ satisfying the equation $\mathbf{s}^6 = -64$.

1.27. For the vector $\cos\theta + \mathbf{j}\sin\theta$, find (a) all the square root vectors, (b) all the cube root vectors, and (c) all the nth root vectors, where n is a positive integer.

1.28. To a two terminal electrical network is applied a sinusoidal voltage of amplitude 4 volts and phase $\pi/6$, and as a result the current entering the positive terminal and leaving the negative terminal oscillates sinusoidally with amplitude 2 amperes and phase $\pi/3$. For both oscillations the frequency is 60 cycles/second and the phases are measured relative to the phase of the same standard oscillation. Draw vector diagrams to represent the voltage and current at time t when (i) $t = 0$, (ii) $t = 5$ milliseconds (iii) $t = 10$ milliseconds, and (iv) $t = 15$ milliseconds. Explain how the time variation of the vectors represents the voltage and current at the terminals.

1.29. For the situation described in Problem 1.28 evaluate the quotient of the voltage vector by the current vector for each of the times indicated, and represent the quotient in a vector diagram. Explain what information is conveyed by the diagram about the relation between the voltage and current oscillations.

1.30. For the situation described in Problem 1.28 evaluate, for each of the times indicated, the planar product of (i) the voltage vector, and (ii) the mirror image of the current vector in the reference axis. Illustrate the result in a vector diagram and explain why the vectors derived in this problem and the previous problem have the same direction.

1.31. For the situation described in Problem 1.28 evaluate the quotient of the current vector by the voltage vector and explain why its direction is the mirror image in the reference axis of the direction of the vector evaluated in Problem 1.29.

1.32. To a mechanical system is applied a sinusoidal force of amplitude 3 newtons and phase $-\pi/4$, and as a result the velocity of the point of application oscillates sinusoidally with amplitude 0.15 meters/second and phase $\pi/6$. For both oscillations the frequency is 0.4 cycles/second and the positive directions for force and velocity are the same. If the force and velocity are represented in a "phase plane" as the reference components of rotating vectors, draw vector diagrams in the phase plane to represent the force and velocity at time t when (i) $t = 0$, (ii) $t = 0.5$ second, (iii) $t = 1.0$ second, and (iv) $t = 1.5$ second.

1.33. For the situation described in Problem 1.32 evaluate, for each of the times indicated, the quotient of the rotating vector whose reference component gives the force by the rotating vector whose reference component gives the velocity, and represent the quotient as a vector in the phase plane. Explain what information is conveyed by the diagram about the relation between the force and velocity oscillations.

1.34. For the situation described in Problem 1.32 evaluate, for each of the times indicated, the planar product of (i) the velocity vector, and (ii) the mirror image of the force vector in the reference axis. Illustrate the result in a vector diagram and explain why the vectors derived in this problem and in the previous problem have the same direction.

1.35. Using the language of complex numbers, reword the statements and solutions of the following problems: 1.3, 1.4, 1.5, 1.6, 1.7, 1.8, 1.9, 1.10.

1.36. A pair of complex numbers such that their real parts are identical in magnitude and sign, while their imaginary parts are identical in magnitude but opposite in sign, are said to be conjugate. Show that any pair of conjugate complex numbers have (i) moduli that are identical, and (ii) arguments that are identical in magnitude and opposite in sign. Using the language of complex numbers, reword the statements and solutions of problems 1.16 and 1.17.

1.37. Using the language of complex numbers, reword the statements and solutions of the following problems: 1.22, 1.23, 1.24, 1.25, 1.26, 1.27.

1.38. In a uniform beam of electrons there are N electrons per unit volume each having energy E. Explain why the probability wave describing the beam has a wave function at each point represented in a phase plane by a rotating vector for which the magnitude is $\sqrt{N}$ and the rate of rotation is proportioned to E. Discuss whether the reference component of this rotating vector has a physical significance.

2. Vector Algebra Using Planar Products and Quotients

2.1. Evaluate the reference and quadrature components of the vector $\mathbf{a}_0 + \mathbf{a}_1\mathbf{s}$ when the vectors $\mathbf{a}_0$, $\mathbf{a}_1$, and $\mathbf{s}$ have each of the sets of values given in the following table. In each case illustrate the process by means of a vector diagram.

a_0	a_1	s
$1 + j3$	$3 + j4$	$6 + j4$
$5 + j5$	$2 - j2$	$4 - j5$
$5 - j6$	$4 + j6$	$-3 + j$
$-4 + j2$	$6 + j5$	$3 - j2$
$-2 + j3$	$5 - j3$	$-5 - j4$

2.2. Evaluate the magnitude and direction of the vector $\mathbf{a}_0 + \mathbf{a}_1\mathbf{s}$ when the vectors $\mathbf{a}_0$, $\mathbf{a}_1$, and $\mathbf{s}$ have each of the sets of values given in the following table. In each case illustrate the process by means of a vector diagram.

a_0	a_1	s
$2\angle\frac{1}{6}\pi$	$6\angle\frac{5}{6}\pi$	$1\angle\frac{3}{4}\pi$
$5\angle 0$	$2\angle-\frac{1}{4}\pi$	$4\angle\frac{5}{6}\pi$
$3\angle-\frac{2}{3}\pi$	$3\angle\pi$	$4\angle\frac{1}{3}\pi$
$2\angle\frac{1}{2}\pi$	$3\angle\frac{1}{3}\pi$	$4\angle-\frac{3}{4}\pi$
$4\angle\frac{1}{6}\pi$	$5\angle-\frac{2}{3}\pi$	$1\angle\frac{1}{4}\pi$

2.3. If **c** and **d** are constant vectors and t is a scalar parameter, show that the tip of the vector $\mathbf{s} = \mathbf{c} + t\mathbf{d}$ describes a straight line. Show further that the tip of the vector $\mathbf{a} + \mathbf{bs}$, where **a** and **b** are constant vectors, describes a straight line through the point whose position vector is $\mathbf{a} + \mathbf{bc}$ in the direction of the vector **bd**.

2.4. Illustrate in a vector diagram the vector addition $10 + 2\mathbf{s} + \mathbf{s}^2$ when the vector **s** has the values: $-1 + j0$, $-1 + j$, $-1 + j2$, $-1 + j3$, and $-1 + j4$.

2.5. Evaluate the reference and quadrature components of the vector $\mathbf{as}^2 + \mathbf{bs} + \mathbf{c}$ when the vectors **a**, **b**, **c**, and **s** have each of the sets of values given in the following table. In each case illustrate the process by means of a vector diagram.

a	b	c	s
6 + j4	1 + j3	6 + j4	1 + j3
2 − j2	−5 + j5	2 − j2	5 + j5
4 + j6	3 − j	−4 + j6	3 − j2
4 − j2	3 + j5	4 − j2	−3 + j5
−2 + j4	5 − j3	2 + j4	5 − j3

2.6. Evaluate the magnitude and direction of the vector $\mathbf{as}^2 + \mathbf{bs} + \mathbf{c}$ when the vectors **a**, **b**, **c**, and **s** have each of the sets of values given in the following table. In each case illustrate the process by means of a vector diagram.

a	b	c	s
$5\angle 0$	$2\angle \pi$	$5\angle \frac{1}{2}\pi$	$3\angle \frac{1}{3}\pi$
$1\angle -\frac{2}{3}\pi$	$6\angle \frac{1}{6}\pi$	$1\angle -\frac{1}{4}\pi$	$6\angle \frac{1}{3}\pi$
$2\angle \frac{5}{6}\pi$	$2\angle -\frac{3}{4}\pi$	$5\angle \frac{1}{4}\pi$	$2\angle -\frac{1}{6}\pi$
$3\angle -\frac{1}{4}\pi$	$5\angle \frac{3}{4}\pi$	$3\angle -\frac{5}{6}\pi$	$4\angle \frac{1}{3}\pi$
$3\angle \frac{1}{2}\pi$	$4\angle -\frac{1}{6}\pi$	$4\angle \frac{2}{3}\pi$	$4\angle -\pi$

2.7. If $\mathbf{s} = x + jy$, show that the vector $10 + 2\mathbf{s} + \mathbf{s}^2$ makes a zero angle with the reference direction if (i) $y = 0$, or (ii) $x = -1$ and $-3 < y < 3$. Show also that the vector $10 + 2\mathbf{s} + \mathbf{s}^2$ makes an angle $\pm\pi$ with the reference direction if (i) $x = -1$ and $y > 3$, or (ii) $x = -1$ and $y < -3$.

2.8. Solve the following quadratic equations for **s**. In each case verify each solution by means of a vector diagram illustrating the vector addition on the left-hand side of the equation.

(a) $\mathbf{s}^2 + 2\mathbf{s} + 10 = 0$
(b) $\mathbf{s}^2 + 2\mathbf{s} + 2 = 0$
(c) $\mathbf{s}^2 + 5\mathbf{s} + 6 = 0$
(d) $\mathbf{s}^2 + 4\mathbf{s} + 5 = 0$
(e) $\mathbf{s}^2 + 4\mathbf{s} + 13 = 0$
(f) $\mathbf{s}^2 + 6\mathbf{s} + 25 = 0$

2.9. Solve the following cubic equations for **s**. In each case verify each solution by means of a vector diagram illustrating the vector addition on the left-hand side of the equation.

(a) $\mathbf{s}^3 + 4\mathbf{s}^2 + 6\mathbf{s} + 4 = 0$
(b) $\mathbf{s}^3 + 4\mathbf{s}^2 + 14\mathbf{s} + 20 = 0$

2.10. If $\mathbf{F}(\mathbf{s})$ is a polynomial function of the vector **s** with scalar coefficients, and **s** is a solution of the equation $\mathbf{F}(\mathbf{s}) = 0$, show that the mirror image $\mathbf{s}^*$ of **s** in the reference axis is also a solution. Hence show that the vectors satisfying the equation either lie along the reference axis or occur in pairs that are mirror images of each other in the reference axis.

2.11. Solve the quadratic equation $\mathbf{a}\mathbf{s}^2 + \mathbf{b}\mathbf{s} + \mathbf{c} = 0$ for **s** when the vectors **a**, **b**, and **c** have each of the sets of values given in the following table. In each case illustrate the process of solution with vector diagrams, and verify the solutions obtained with vector diagrams.

a	b	c
1 + j0	−2 − j3	−1 + j3
1 + j0	−3 − j2	1 + j3
1 + j	1 − j	−2 + j4
1 − j	−3 − j3	−4 + j2
1 + j2	−1 + j8	3 + j11
1 − j2	1 − j7	10 − j15

2.12. Evaluate the magnitude and direction of the vector $(\mathbf{s} - \mathbf{s}_1)(\mathbf{s} - \mathbf{s}_2)$ when the vectors $\mathbf{s}_1$, $\mathbf{s}_2$, and **s** have each of the sets of values given in the following table. In each case illustrate the process by means of a vector diagram.

$\mathbf{s}_1$	$\mathbf{s}_2$	**s**
1 + j3	1 − j3	3 + j4
6 + j4	6 − j4	4 − j5
−2 + j0	−4 + j0	5 + j6
−1 + j0	−2 + j0	0 + j4
3 − j2	6 + j5	−4 − j2
−5 − j4	5 − j3	−2 + j3

2.13. Evaluate the reference and quadrature components of the vector $(\mathbf{s} - \mathbf{s}_1)(\mathbf{s} - \mathbf{s}_2)$ when the vectors $\mathbf{s}_1$, $\mathbf{s}_2$, and $\mathbf{s}$ have each of the sets of values given in the following table. In each case illustrate the process by means of a vector diagram.

$\mathbf{s}_1$	$\mathbf{s}_2$	$\mathbf{s}$
$4\underline{/\frac{3}{4}\pi}$	$3\underline{/-\frac{2}{3}\pi}$	$5\underline{/\frac{1}{2}\pi}$
$2\underline{/\frac{2}{3}\pi}$	$2\underline{/-\frac{2}{3}\pi}$	$4\underline{/\frac{3}{4}\pi}$
$5\underline{/0}$	$3\underline{/\pi}$	$4\underline{/\frac{5}{6}\pi}$
$4\underline{/\pi}$	$2\underline{/-\pi}$	$6\underline{/\frac{1}{2}\pi}$
$1\underline{/\frac{1}{4}\pi}$	$5\underline{/-\frac{2}{3}\pi}$	$4\underline{/\frac{1}{6}\pi}$
$4\underline{/\frac{1}{3}\pi}$	$3\underline{/-\frac{5}{6}\pi}$	$2\underline{/\frac{1}{6}\pi}$

2.14. Evaluate the magnitude and direction of the vector

$$\frac{1}{(\mathbf{s} - \mathbf{s}_1)(\mathbf{s} - \mathbf{s}_2)}$$

when the vectors $\mathbf{s}_1$, $\mathbf{s}_2$, and $\mathbf{s}$ have each of the sets of values given in the following table. In each case illustrate the process by means of a vector diagram.

$\mathbf{s}_1$	$\mathbf{s}_2$	$\mathbf{s}$
$-2 + j3$	$-2 - j3$	$0 + j5$
$-5 + j4$	$-5 - j4$	$-4 - j2$
$3 - j$	$3 + j$	$4 + j6$
$-1 + j0$	$-2 + j0$	$0 + j5$
$5 + j6$	$-4 + j0$	$-2 + j0$
$4 - j5$	$6 - j4$	$6 + j4$

2.15. Evaluate the reference and quadrature components of the vector

$$\frac{1}{(\mathbf{s} - \mathbf{s}_1)(\mathbf{s} - \mathbf{s}_2)}$$

when the vectors $\mathbf{s}_1$, $\mathbf{s}_2$, and $\mathbf{s}$ have each of the sets of values given in the following table. In each case illustrate the process by means of a vector diagram.

$\mathbf{s}_1$	$\mathbf{s}_2$	$\mathbf{s}$
$4\underline{/\tfrac{2}{3}\pi}$	$4\underline{/-\tfrac{2}{3}\pi}$	$4\underline{/-\pi}$
$3\underline{/\tfrac{5}{6}\pi}$	$3\underline{/-\tfrac{5}{6}\pi}$	$4\underline{/-\tfrac{1}{6}\pi}$
$5\underline{/\tfrac{1}{4}\pi}$	$5\underline{/-\tfrac{1}{4}\pi}$	$3\underline{/\tfrac{1}{2}\pi}$
$2\underline{/-\pi}$	$3\underline{/\pi}$	$4\underline{/\tfrac{1}{3}\pi}$
$2\underline{/-\tfrac{5}{6}\pi}$	$6\underline{/\tfrac{1}{3}\pi}$	$2\underline{/-\tfrac{1}{6}\pi}$
$1\underline{/\tfrac{1}{6}\pi}$	$3\underline{/\tfrac{1}{3}\pi}$	$5\underline{/\tfrac{1}{4}\pi}$

2.16. Evaluate the magnitude and direction of the vector

$$\frac{\mathbf{s} - \mathbf{s}_0}{(\mathbf{s} - \mathbf{s}_1)(\mathbf{s} - \mathbf{s}_2)}$$

when the vectors $\mathbf{s}_0$, $\mathbf{s}_1$, $\mathbf{s}_2$, and $\mathbf{s}$ have each of the sets of values given in the following table. In each case illustrate the process by means of a vector diagram.

$\mathbf{s}_0$	$\mathbf{s}_1$	$\mathbf{s}_2$	$\mathbf{s}$
$-1 + j0$	$-2 + j3$	$-2 - j3$	$0 + j5$
$-2 + j0$	$-5 + j4$	$-5 - j4$	$-4 - j2$
$2 + j0$	$3 - j$	$3 + j$	$4 + j6$
$3 + j2$	$-1 + j0$	$-2 + j0$	$0 + j5$
$3 - j4$	$5 + j6$	$-4 + j0$	$-2 + j0$
$-5 + j4$	$4 - j5$	$6 - j4$	$6 + j4$

2.17. Evaluate the reference and quadrature components of the vector

$$\frac{\mathbf{s} - \mathbf{s}_0}{(\mathbf{s} - \mathbf{s}_1)(\mathbf{s} - \mathbf{s}_2)}$$

when the vectors $\mathbf{s}_0$, $\mathbf{s}_1$, $\mathbf{s}_2$, and $\mathbf{s}$ have each of the sets of values given in the following table. In each case illustrate the process by means of a vector diagram.

s_0	s_1	s_2	s
$2\underline{/\pi}$	$4\underline{/\frac{2}{3}\pi}$	$4\underline{/-\frac{2}{3}\pi}$	$4\underline{/-\pi}$
$1\underline{/-\pi}$	$3\underline{/\frac{5}{6}\pi}$	$3\underline{/-\frac{5}{6}\pi}$	$4\underline{/-\frac{1}{6}\pi}$
$3\underline{/0}$	$5\underline{/\frac{1}{4}\pi}$	$5\underline{/-\frac{1}{4}\pi}$	$3\underline{/\frac{1}{2}\pi}$
$5\underline{/\frac{1}{3}\pi}$	$2\underline{/-\pi}$	$3\underline{/\pi}$	$4\underline{/\frac{1}{3}\pi}$
$4\underline{/-\frac{1}{2}\pi}$	$2\underline{/-\frac{5}{6}\pi}$	$6\underline{/\frac{1}{3}\pi}$	$2\underline{/-\frac{1}{6}\pi}$
$3\underline{/\frac{3}{4}\pi}$	$1\underline{/-\frac{1}{4}\pi}$	$3\underline{/\frac{1}{3}\pi}$	$5\underline{/\frac{1}{4}\pi}$

2.18. A vector s can take the following values: $-1 + j0$, $-1 + j$, $-1 + j2$, $-1 + j3$, and $-1 + j4$. For these values of s, evaluate the following vectors in magnitude and direction illustrating the process by means of vector diagrams:

(a) $\dfrac{1}{s^2 + 2s + 10}$

(b) $\dfrac{1}{s^2 + 2s + 2}$

(e) $\dfrac{s}{s^2 + 5s + 6}$

(d) $\dfrac{s + 1}{s^2 + 4s + 5}$

(e) $\dfrac{2s + 3}{s^2 + 4s + 13}$

(f) $\dfrac{s^2 + 2s + 2}{s^2 + 6s + 25}$

(g) $\dfrac{s + 1}{s^3 + 4s^2 + 6s + 4}$

(h) $\dfrac{s^2 + 2s + 10}{s^3 + 4s^2 + 14s + 20}$

3. Graphical Representation of Vector Functions of a Vector

3.1. Sketch a contour map in the s plane illustrating as functions of s the magnitude and direction of the vector $\mathbf{a}(s - s_0)$ where the vectors $\mathbf{a}$ and s_0 have the pairs of values given in the following table. In each case sketch curves showing the cross sections of the contour map along the reference and quadrature axes, and deduce analytical expressions for these curves.

a:	$1\underline{/\frac{1}{6}\pi}$	$1\underline{/-\frac{2}{3}\pi}$	$3\underline{/-\frac{1}{4}\pi}$	$3\underline{/\frac{5}{6}\pi}$	$5\underline{/\frac{1}{3}\pi}$
s_0:	$2\underline{/\frac{1}{2}\pi}$	$5\underline{/-\frac{3}{4}\pi}$	$2\underline{/-\pi}$	$4\underline{/\pi}$	$4\underline{/-\frac{2}{3}\pi}$

3.2. Sketch a contour map in the $\mathbf{s}$ plane illustrating as functions of $\mathbf{s}$ the magnitude and direction of the vector $\mathbf{a}/(\mathbf{s} - \mathbf{s}_0)$ where the vectors $\mathbf{a}$ and $\mathbf{s}_0$ have the pairs of values given in the following table. In each case sketch curves showing the cross sections of the contour map along the reference and quadrature axes, and deduce analytical expressions for these curves.

a:	$2\underline{/0}$	$2\underline{/\tfrac{1}{4}\pi}$	$4\underline{/-\tfrac{1}{2}\pi}$	$2\underline{/\tfrac{1}{3}\pi}$	$4\underline{/-\tfrac{1}{6}\pi}$
$\mathbf{s}_0$:	$3\underline{/\tfrac{5}{6}\pi}$	$3\underline{/-\tfrac{1}{2}\pi}$	$6\underline{/\pi}$	$5\underline{/-\tfrac{2}{3}\pi}$	$3\underline{/\tfrac{3}{4}\pi}$

3.3. Sketch a contour map in the $\mathbf{s}$ plane illustrating as functions of $\mathbf{s}$ the magnitude and direction of the vector $1/(\mathbf{s}+1)$. Sketch curves showing the variation along the reference axis of the magnitude and direction of the vector $1/(\mathbf{s} + 1)$. Sketch also the graph of the scalar quantity $1/(s + 1)$ as a function of the scalar variable s. Explain the relation between this graph and the cross section of the contour map along the reference axis.

3.4. In the $\mathbf{s}$ plane the magnitude and direction of the vector $(\mathbf{s} - \mathbf{s}_1)/(\mathbf{s} - \mathbf{s}_2)$, where $\mathbf{s}_1$ and $\mathbf{s}_2$ are fixed vectors, are to be illustrated by means of a contour map. Show that the angle contours are arcs of circles through the points whose position vectors are $\mathbf{s}_1$ and $\mathbf{s}_2$. Show also that the magnitude contours form a system of coaxal circles for which the limiting points are at the locations $\mathbf{s}_1$ and $\mathbf{s}_2$.

3.5. In the $\mathbf{s}$ plane make a drawing of the contour map that illustrates as functions of $\mathbf{s}$ the magnitude and direction of the vector $(\mathbf{s} - 1)/(\mathbf{s} + 1)$. Mark the angle contours at suitable equal intervals of the angle. Mark the magnitude contours at suitable equal intervals of (a) the magnitude, and (b) the logarithm of the magnitude (Carter diagram).

3.6. In the previous problem sketch curves showing the variation along the reference axis of the magnitude and direction of the vector $(\mathbf{s} - 1)/(\mathbf{s} + 1)$ and relate them to the graph of the scalar quantity $(s - 1)/(s + 1)$ as a function of the scalar variable s.

3.7. In the $\mathbf{s}$ plane the magnitude and direction of the vector $\mathbf{s}^2 + 3\mathbf{s} + 2$ are to be illustrated as functions of $\mathbf{s}$ by means of a contour map. Express the vector in the form $(\mathbf{s} - \mathbf{s}_1)(\mathbf{s} - \mathbf{s}_2)$ where $\mathbf{s}_1$ and $\mathbf{s}_2$ are constant vectors and hence sketch the behavior of the map near the points whose position vectors are $\mathbf{s}_1$ and $\mathbf{s}_2$. Examine the magnitude and angle contours through the point whose position vector is $\frac{1}{2}(s_1 + s_2)$, and hence complete a sketch of the contour map.

3.8. Repeat the previous problem for each of the following vector functions of s:

(a) $s^2 + 4s + 3$
(b) $s^2 + 6s + 8$
(c) $s^2 + 9s + 20$
(d) $s^2 + 7s + 10$
(e) $s^2 + 5s + 6$
(f) $s^2 + 2s + 10$
(g) $s^2 + 2s + 2$
(h) $s^2 + 4s + 5$
(i) $s^2 + 4s + 13$
(j) $s^2 + 6s + 25$

3.9. In the s plane sketch a contour map illustrating as functions of s the magnitude and direction of each of the following vectors:

(a) $s^3 + 6s^2 + 11s + 6$
(b) $s^3 + 8s^2 + 19s + 12$
(c) $s^3 + 4s^2 + 6s + 4$
(d) $s^3 + 4s^2 + 14s + 20$
(e) $s^2 + 4s + 4$
(f) $s^3 + 4s^2 + 5s + 2$
(g) $s^4 + 10s^3 + 35s^2 + 50s + 24$

3.10. Analyze into partial fractions each of the following vector functions of s:

(a) $\dfrac{1}{s^2 + 4s + 3}$

(b) $\dfrac{1}{s^2 + 6s + 8}$

(c) $\dfrac{s}{s^2 + 9s + 20}$

(d) $\dfrac{s + 3}{s^2 + 7s + 10}$

(e) $\dfrac{s^2 + 5s + 4}{s^2 + 5s + 6}$

(f) $\dfrac{1}{s^2 + 2s + 10}$

(g) $\dfrac{1}{s^2 + 2s + 2}$

(h) $\dfrac{s}{s^2 + 4s + 5}$

(i) $\dfrac{s + 1}{s^2 + 4s + 13}$

(j) $\dfrac{s^2 + 6s + 8}{s^2 + 6s + 25}$

(k) $\dfrac{1}{s^2 + 4s + 4}$

(l) $\dfrac{1}{s^3 + 6s^2 + 11s + 6}$

(m) $\dfrac{s + 2}{s^3 + 8s^2 + 19s + 12}$

(n) $\dfrac{1}{s^3 + 4s^2 + 6s + 4}$

(o) $\dfrac{s}{s^3 + 4s^2 + 14s + 20}$

(p) $\dfrac{1}{s^3 + 4s^2 + 5s + 2}$

(q) $\dfrac{s}{s^4 + 10s^3 + 35s^2 + 50s + 24}$

3.11. In the s plane the magnitude and direction of the vector $1/(s^2 + 3s + 2)$ are to be illustrated as functions of s by means of a contour map. Express the vector in the form $1/(s - s_1)(s - s_2)$ where s_1 and s_2 are constant vectors, and hence sketch the behavior of the map near the points whose position vectors are s_1 and s_2. Examine the magnitude and angle contours through the point $\frac{1}{2}(s_1 + s_2)$, and hence complete a sketch of the contour map.

3.12. Repeat the previous problem for each of the vector functions of s obtained by taking the reciprocals of the expressions listed in Problem 3.8.

3.13. In the s plane sketch a contour map illustrating as functions of s the magnitude and direction of each of the following vectors:

(a) $\dfrac{s}{s^2 + 9s + 20}$ (e) $\dfrac{s + 2}{s^3 + 8s^2 + 19s + 12}$

(b) $\dfrac{s + 3}{s^2 + 7s + 10}$ (f) $\dfrac{s}{s^3 + 4s^2 + 14s + 20}$

(c) $\dfrac{s}{s^2 + 4s + 5}$ (g) $\dfrac{s}{s^4 + 10s^3 + 35s^2 + 50s + 24}$

(d) $\dfrac{s + 1}{s^2 + 4s + 13}$

3.14. In the s plane sketch a contour map illustrating as functions of s the magnitude and direction of the reciprocals of each of the vectors listed in the previous problem.

3.15. In the s plane sketch a contour map illustrating as functions of s the magnitude and direction of each of the following vectors. In each case sketch also a contour map illustrating the reciprocal of the vector.

(a) $\dfrac{s^2 + 5s + 4}{s^2 + 5s + 6}$ (b) $\dfrac{s^2 + 6s + 8}{s^2 + 6s + 25}$ (c) $\dfrac{s^2 + 4s + 5}{s^2 + 4s + 13}$

3.16. In the diagram a circle is drawn with opposite ends of a

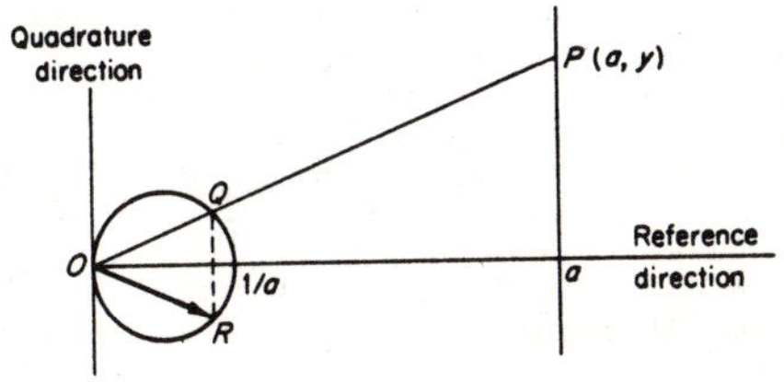

diameter at the origin and at the point $1/a$ on the reference axis. P is a point that can move along a straight line parallel to the quadrature axis and that has Cartesian coordinates (a, y). The join of O to P intersects the circle in Q, and R is the mirror image of Q in the reference direction. Prove that the variations with y of the magnitude and angle of the vector $\overrightarrow{OR}$ give the resonance curves.

3.17. Illustrate graphically the variation along the quadrature axis in the s plane of the magnitude and direction of each of the following vectors:

(a) $\dfrac{2\mathbf{s}}{\mathbf{s}^2 + 2\mathbf{s} + 101}$ (b) $\dfrac{20}{\mathbf{s}^2 + 2\mathbf{s} + 101}$ (c) $\dfrac{2\mathbf{s} + 1}{\mathbf{s}^2 + 2\mathbf{s} + 101}$

3.18. Explain how a function $\mathbf{F}(\mathbf{s})$ may be illustrated in the s plane by means of a contour map in which one set of contours are the curves on which the reference component of $\mathbf{F}(\mathbf{s})$ has a series of constant values and the other set of contours are the curves on which the quadrature component of $\mathbf{F}(\mathbf{s})$ has a series of constant values. Illustrate the explanation by taking $\mathbf{F}(\mathbf{s}) = 1/\mathbf{s}$.

3.19. In the s plane make a drawing of the contour map that illustrates as functions of s the reference and quadrature components of the vector $(1 - \mathbf{s})/\mathbf{s}$. Show that the reference and quadrature contours are circles, and mark the contours at suitable equal intervals. Show further that, if contours corresponding to negative values of the reference component are omitted, the diagram is enclosed in a circle with the join of the points $\mathbf{s} = 0$ and $\mathbf{s} = 1$ as diameter (Smith diagram).

4. The Exponential Function of a Vector

4.1. Draw vector diagrams to illustrate the vector summation represented by the infinite series

$$1 + \mathbf{s} + \frac{1}{2!}\mathbf{s}^2 + \frac{1}{3!}\mathbf{s}^3 + \cdots$$

when $\mathbf{s} = \mathbf{j}\theta$ and θ has the values: 0, 0.1, 0.2, 0.3, 0.4, 0.5, and 2.0 radians.

4.2. Draw a vector diagram to illustrate the truth of the equation

$$\frac{1}{1 - \mathbf{s}} = 1 + \mathbf{s} + \mathbf{s}^2 + \cdots$$

for a vector **s** whose magnitude is less than unity. Discuss whether the equation is true for a vector **s** whose magnitude is greater than unity. Draw a contour map in the **s** plane to illustrate (i) the vector on the left-hand side of the equation, and (ii) the vector on the right-hand side of the equation, explaining the difference between the two contour maps.

4.3. Repeat the previous problem for the equation

$$\frac{1}{(1 - \mathbf{s})^2} = 1 + 2\mathbf{s} + 3\mathbf{s}^2 + \cdots$$

4.4. Write down the series expansions for the hyperbolic cosine and hyperbolic sine functions of a scalar quantity. Hence suggest appropriate nomenclature for the two vectors

$$1 + \frac{\mathbf{s}^2}{2!} + \frac{\mathbf{s}^4}{4!} + \frac{\mathbf{s}^6}{6!} + \cdots$$

and

$$\mathbf{s} + \frac{\mathbf{s}^3}{3!} + \frac{\mathbf{s}^5}{5!} + \frac{\mathbf{s}^7}{7!} + \cdots.$$

4.5. Show that the vector functions of **s** defined in the preceding problem may be expressed as $\frac{1}{2}(e^{\mathbf{s}} + e^{-\mathbf{s}})$ and $\frac{1}{2}(e^{\mathbf{s}} - e^{-\mathbf{s}})$.

4.6. Write down the series expansions for the cosine and sine functions of a scalar quantity. Hence suggest appropriate nomenclature for the two vectors

$$1 - \frac{\mathbf{s}^2}{2!} + \frac{\mathbf{s}^4}{4!} - \frac{\mathbf{s}^6}{6!} \cdots$$

$$\mathbf{s} - \frac{\mathbf{s}^3}{3!} + \frac{\mathbf{s}^5}{5!} - \frac{\mathbf{s}^7}{7!} \cdots.$$

Evaluate the reference and quadrature components of these two vectors to three significant figures if $\mathbf{s} = 0.2 \angle 30°$.

4.7. Show that the vector functions of **s** defined in the preceding problem may be expressed as $\frac{1}{2}(e^{\mathbf{j}\mathbf{s}} + e^{-\mathbf{j}\mathbf{s}})$ and $(1/2\mathbf{j})(e^{\mathbf{j}\mathbf{s}} - e^{-\mathbf{j}\mathbf{s}})$.

4.8. Illustrate in a vector diagram the pairs of vectors **A** and **B** given in the following table. For each pair, calculate the vectors **A** + **B**, **A** − **B**, **AB**, and **A**/**B**. Express each of these vectors in exponential form and illustrate it in a vector diagram.

A:	$2e^{\mathrm{j}\frac{1}{6}\pi}$	$3e^{-\mathrm{j}\frac{2}{3}\pi}$	$2e^{\mathrm{j}\frac{1}{2}\pi}$	$4e^{-\mathrm{j}\frac{2}{3}\pi}$	$e^{-\mathrm{j}\pi}$
B:	$6e^{\mathrm{j}\frac{5}{6}\pi}$	$2e^{-\mathrm{j}\frac{1}{4}\pi}$	$3e^{\mathrm{j}\pi}$	$4e^{\mathrm{j}\frac{5}{6}\pi}$	$3e^{-\mathrm{j}\frac{3}{4}\pi}$

4.9. For integral values of n explain why

$$(\cos\theta + \mathrm{j}\sin\theta)^n = \cos n\theta + \mathrm{j}\sin n\theta$$

and illustrate the significance of the equation in a vector diagram.

4.10. Show that the nth roots of a unit vector in the reference direction are given by the vectors $e^{\mathrm{j}2\pi r/n}$ where $r = 0, 1, \ldots, n-1$, and illustrate the vectors in a vector diagram.

4.11. For integral values of n calculate the various possible magnitudes and directions of the vector $(-1)^{1/n}$ and illustrate them in a vector diagram.

4.12. If $\mathbf{s} = \sigma + \mathrm{j}\omega$, draw a vector diagram to illustrate the time variation of the vector $e^{\mathbf{s}t}$ when ω corresponds to a frequency of 60 cycles/second, and σ has the following values in nepers/second: 0, ±50, ±100. In each case draw a curve to illustrate the time variation of the reference component of the vector $e^{\mathbf{s}t}$.

4.13. Repeat the previous problem when σ has the following values in decibles/millisecond: 0, ±1, ±2.

4.14. Repeat Problem 4.12 when the magnitude of the actance vector **s** is 1 millisecond^{-1} and the counterclockwise angle of the actance vector measured from the increment axis has the following values in radians: 0, $\pm\frac{1}{6}\pi$, $\pm\frac{1}{3}\pi$, $\pm\frac{1}{2}\pi$, $\pm\frac{2}{3}\pi$, $\pm\frac{3}{4}\pi$, $\pm\frac{5}{6}\pi$, $\pm\pi$. In each case demonstrate the relation between the angle of the actance vector and the angle of the equiangular spiral.

4.15. An oscillation has an amplitude that is equal to A at time zero and that increases exponentially at the rate σ nepers/second. The frequency is f cycles/second and the phase is α radians. For each of the sets of values of A, σ, f and α given in the following table, calculate (i) the magnitude and direction of the vector amplitude, and (ii) the reference and quadrature components of the actance. Hence write an analytical expression for the spiraling vector whose reference component represents the oscillation. Illustrate the spiraling vector in a vector diagram for values of the time equal to the following fractions of a period: 0, $\frac{1}{6}$, $\frac{1}{3}$, $\frac{1}{2}$, $\frac{2}{3}$, $\frac{5}{6}$, and 1.

A:	10	10^{-1}	10^{-2}	10^{-4}	10^{-6}
σ:	0	-23.5	-1.59×10^3	-2.75×10^5	9.1×10^6
f:	60	256	10^4	10^6	10^8
α:	$\frac{1}{6}\pi$	$-\frac{1}{4}\pi$	π	$-\frac{5}{6}\pi$	$\frac{3}{6}\pi$

4.16. Sketch a contour map in an actance diagram for the magnitude and direction of the vector $e^{\mathbf{s}t}$ (i) when t has a fixed negative value, and (ii) when t has a fixed positive value. Designate by a letter H the region where the magnitude of the vector is large compared with unity, and by a letter L the region where the magnitude of the vector is small compared with unity. Sketch curves to illustrate, for a fixed positive value of t, the variation along the frequency axis of the magnitude and angle of the vector $e^{\mathbf{s}t}$.

4.17. Repeat Problem 4.16 for the vector $(1/\mathbf{s})e^{\mathbf{s}t}$.

4.18. Repeat Problem 4.16 for vector $(\mathbf{s} - \mathbf{s}_0)^{-1}e^{\mathbf{s}t}$ when the tip of the fixed vector $\mathbf{s}_0$ lies on the decrement axis.

4.19. Repeat Problem 4.16 for the vector $\mathbf{F}(\mathbf{s})e^{\mathbf{s}t}$ when $\mathbf{F}(\mathbf{s})$ is given by each of the expressions in Problem 3.13.

5. Additional Problems

5.1. If $\mathbf{s}$ denotes position vector in an actance diagram, define the vectors cosh $\mathbf{s}$, sinh $\mathbf{s}$, cos $\mathbf{s}$, and sin $\mathbf{s}$. Sketch contour maps in the $\mathbf{s}$ plane for the magnitudes and angles of these functions.

5.2. Specify the locations in the $\mathbf{s}$ plane of the zeros of the functions in the previous problem. Sketch curves showing the cross sections of the functions along (a) the reference axis, and (b) the quadrature axis.

5.3. Establish the vector identities

$$\cosh \mathbf{js} = \cos \mathbf{s}$$
$$\sinh \mathbf{js} = \mathbf{j} \sin \mathbf{s}$$

and illustrate their significance with the aid of the contour maps in the **s** plane of the functions cosh **s**, sinh **s**, cos **s**, and sin **s**.

5.4. Sketch contour maps in the **s** plane for the functions $\cosh^2 \mathbf{s}$ and $\sinh^2 \mathbf{s}$. Establish analytically the vector identity

$$\cosh^2 \mathbf{s} - \sinh^2 \mathbf{s} = 1$$

and verify its truth with the aid of the contour maps.

5.5. Sketch contour maps in the **s** plane for the functions $\cos^2 \mathbf{s}$ and $\sin^2 \mathbf{s}$. Establish analytically the vector identity

$$\cos^2 \mathbf{s} + \sin^2 \mathbf{s} = 1$$

and verify its truth with the aid of the contour maps.

5.6. Establish the following identities and describe their vector significance:

$$\cosh 2\mathbf{s} = \cosh^2 \mathbf{s} + \sinh^2 \mathbf{s} = 2\cosh^2 \mathbf{s} - 1 = 1 + 2\sinh^2 \mathbf{s}$$
$$\cos 2\mathbf{s} = \cos^2 \mathbf{s} - \sin^2 \mathbf{s} = 2\cos^2 \mathbf{s} - 1 = 1 - 2\sin^2 \mathbf{s}$$
$$\sinh 2\mathbf{s} = 2 \sinh \mathbf{s} \cosh \mathbf{s}$$
$$\sin 2\mathbf{s} = 2 \sin \mathbf{s} \cos \mathbf{s}$$
$$\cosh(\mathbf{s}_1 \pm \mathbf{s}_2) = \cosh \mathbf{s}_1 \cosh \mathbf{s}_2 \pm \sinh \mathbf{s}_1 \sinh \mathbf{s}_2$$
$$\sinh(\mathbf{s}_1 \pm \mathbf{s}_2) = \sinh \mathbf{s}_1 \cosh \mathbf{s}_2 \pm \cosh \mathbf{s}_1 \sinh \mathbf{s}_2$$
$$\cos(\mathbf{s}_1 \pm \mathbf{s}_2) = \cos \mathbf{s}_1 \cos \mathbf{s}_2 \mp \sin \mathbf{s}_1 \sin \mathbf{s}_2$$
$$\sin(\mathbf{s}_1 \pm \mathbf{s}_2) = \sin \mathbf{s}_1 \cos \mathbf{s}_2 \pm \cos \mathbf{s}_1 \sin \mathbf{s}_2$$

5.7. If $\mathbf{s} = x + \mathbf{j}y$, show that:

(i) The vector cosh **s** has reference and quadrature components $(\cosh x \cos y, \sinh x \sin y)$.

(ii) The vector sinh **s** has reference and quadrature components $(\sinh x \cos y, \cosh x \sin y)$.

(iii) The vector cos **s** has reference and quadrature components $(\cos x \cosh y, -\sin x \sinh y)$.

(iv) The vector sin **s** has reference and quadrature components $(\sin x \cosh y, \cos x \sinh y)$.

5.8. If $\mathbf{s} = x + \mathbf{j}y$, show that:

(i) The vector cosh **s** has magnitude $(\cosh^2 x + \sin^2 y)^{1/2}$ and makes with the reference direction a counterclockwise angle $\tan^{-1}(\tanh x \tan y)$.

(ii) The vector sinh **s** has magnitude $(\cosh^2 x + \cos^2 y)^{1/2}$ and makes with the reference direction a counter-clockwise angle $\tan^{-1}(\coth x \tan y)$.

(iii) The vector cos **s** has magnitude $(\sin^2 x + \cosh^2 y)^{1/2}$ and makes with the reference direction a counter-clockwise angle $-\tan^{-1}(\tan x \tanh y)$.

(iv) The vector sinh **s** has magnitude $(\cos^2 x + \cosh^2 y)^{1/2}$ and makes with the reference direction a counter-clockwise angle $\tan^{-1}(\cot x \tanh y)$.

5.9. A vector function **F** of a vector **s** is represented by a contour map in the **s** plane. Displacement from the point **s** in the plane to the point $\mathbf{s} + d\mathbf{s}$ results in the vector **F** changing to the vector $\mathbf{F} + d\mathbf{F}$. The quotient vector

$$\frac{d\mathbf{F}}{d\mathbf{s}}$$

is formed, and it may be assumed that this vector tends to a limiting vector as the magnitude of the displacement vector $d\mathbf{s}$ tends to zero regardless of its direction. If the limiting vector is called the derivative of **F** with respect to **s**, and if a function for which the derivative may be calculated is called an analytic function, show that the derivatives of analytic vector functions of a vector may be calculated by the same rules as the derivatives of analytic scalar functions of a scalar.

5.10. The function $\mathbf{F}(\mathbf{s}) = \mathbf{s} - \mathbf{s}_0$, where $\mathbf{s}_0$ is a fixed vector, is represented by means of a contour map in the **s** plane. Using the definition of a derivative as a limiting process, explain why the vector $d\mathbf{F}/d\mathbf{s}$ is, at all points in the **s** plane, a unit vector in the reference direction.

5.11. Calculate the derivatives of the functions $e_{\mathbf{s}}$, cosh **s**, sinh **s**, cos **s**, and sin **s**.

5.12. If **s** is a variable vector and $\mathbf{s}_0$ a fixed vector, calculate the derivative of the function,

$$\frac{1}{\mathbf{s} - \mathbf{s}_0}$$

at all points in the **s** plane at which this is possible. Explain why the function is not analytic at the point $\mathbf{s} = \mathbf{s}_0$.

5.13. Two maps of the world are drawn on a flat sheet of paper using different projections. An origin and an initial line are chosen in the sheet, and each place in the world is located by means of its position vector **r** in one map and **s** in the other. If the position vectors **r** and **s** are analytic functions of each other, show that the magnitude of the vector $d\mathbf{s}/d\mathbf{r}$ evaluated for a particular place in the world is the scale ratio for the maps at that location. Give an interpretation for the angle of the vector $d\mathbf{s}/d\mathbf{r}$ and of the way in which it varies from place to place.

5.14. A function $\mathbf{F}(\mathbf{s})$ is represented in the **s** plane by means of a contour map. Explain why, at a saddle point in the contour map, $d\mathbf{F}/d\mathbf{s} = 0$.

5.15. The function

$$\mathbf{F}(\mathbf{s}) = \mathbf{a}(\mathbf{s} - \mathbf{s}_1)(\mathbf{s} - \mathbf{s}_2)$$

where $\mathbf{a}$, $\mathbf{s}_1$, and $\mathbf{s}_2$ are fixed vectors, is represented by means of a contour map in the **s** plane. Show that there is a saddle point at the location $\frac{1}{2}(\mathbf{s}_1 + \mathbf{s}_2)$, and sketch the contour map.

5.16. Calculate the location of the saddle point in the **s** plane for each of the following functions, and sketch the contour map:

(a) $\mathbf{s}^2 + 4\mathbf{s} + 3$
(b) $\mathbf{s}^2 + 6\mathbf{s} + 8$
(c) $\mathbf{s}^2 + 9\mathbf{s} + 20$
(d) $\mathbf{s}^2 + 7\mathbf{s} + 10$
(e) $\mathbf{s}^2 + 5\mathbf{s} + 6$
(f) $\mathbf{s}^2 + 2\mathbf{s} + 10$
(g) $\mathbf{s}^2 + 2\mathbf{s} + 2$
(h) $\mathbf{s}^2 + 4\mathbf{s} + 5$
(i) $\mathbf{s}^2 + 4\mathbf{s} + 13$
(j) $\mathbf{s}^2 + 6\mathbf{s} + 25$

5.17. The function

$$\mathbf{F}(\mathbf{s}) = \frac{\mathbf{a}}{(\mathbf{s} - \mathbf{s}_1)(\mathbf{s} - \mathbf{s}_2)}$$

where $\mathbf{a}$, $\mathbf{s}_1$, and $\mathbf{s}_2$ are fixed vectors, is represented by means of a contour map in the **s** plane. Show that there is a saddle point at the location $\frac{1}{2}(\mathbf{s}_1 + \mathbf{s}_2)$ and sketch the contour map.

5.18. For each of the functions obtained by taking the reciprocals of the vectors listed in Problem 3.9, calculate the location of the saddle point in the **s** plane, and sketch the contour map.

5.19. Calculate the location of the saddle points in the $\mathbf{s}$ plane for each of the following functions, and sketch the contour map:

(a) $\mathbf{s}^3 + 6\mathbf{s}^2 + 11\mathbf{s} + 6$

(b) $\mathbf{s}^3 + 4\mathbf{s}^2 + 6\mathbf{s} + 4$

(c) $\dfrac{1}{\mathbf{s}^3 + 8\mathbf{s}^2 + 19\mathbf{s} + 12}$

(d) $\dfrac{1}{\mathbf{s}^3 + 4\mathbf{s}^2 + 14\mathbf{s} + 20}$

(e) $\dfrac{\mathbf{s}}{\mathbf{s}^2 + 9\mathbf{s} + 20}$

(f) $\dfrac{\mathbf{s} + 3}{\mathbf{s}^2 + 7\mathbf{s} + 10}$

(g) $\dfrac{\mathbf{s}}{\mathbf{s}^2 + 4\mathbf{s} + 5}$

(h) $\dfrac{\mathbf{s} + 1}{\mathbf{s}^2 + 4\mathbf{s} + 13}$

5.20. Sketch the form of the contour map in the $\mathbf{s}$ plane for the planar product of $e^{\mathbf{s}t}$ with each of the functions referred to in Problems 5.18 and 5.19, distinguishing between the cases when (i) $t < 0$, and (ii) $t > 0$.

5.21. For the contour maps for the functions cos $\mathbf{s}$ and sin $\mathbf{s}$ demonstrate that the saddle points in each map coincide with the zeros in the other map.

5.22. A function of the vector $\mathbf{s}$ is defined by

$$\mathbf{F}(\mathbf{s}) = \log_e \mathbf{s}$$

where the logarithmic operator is the inverse of the exponential operator. By considering the vector $e^{\mathbf{F}}$, show that the reference component of $\mathbf{F}(\mathbf{s})$ is $\log_e |\mathbf{s}|$ and the quadrature component is $\angle\mathbf{s}$. Sketch a contour map in the $\mathbf{s}$ plane for the reference and quadrature components of $\log_e \mathbf{s}$, and derive a contour map for the magnitude and direction of $\log_e \mathbf{s}$.

5.23. From the previous problem deduce that, if $\mathbf{F}(\mathbf{s})$ and $\mathbf{G}(\mathbf{s})$ are two functions of the vector $\mathbf{s}$ such that

$$\mathbf{F}(\mathbf{s}) = \log_e \mathbf{G}(\mathbf{s})$$

then the reference and quadrature components of $\mathbf{F}(\mathbf{s})$ are $\log_e |\mathbf{G}(\mathbf{s})|$ and $\angle\mathbf{G}(\mathbf{s})$, respectively. Deduce that the contour map in the $\mathbf{s}$ plane giving the reference and quadrature components of the function $\mathbf{F}(\mathbf{s})$ involves the same contours as the contour map giving the magnitude and direction of the function $\mathbf{G}(\mathbf{s})$. Explain the relation between the contour markings in the two cases.

5.24. In a system of rectangular Cartesian coordinates in a plane, **s** denotes the position vector of the point (x, y) with respect to the origin. A vector function of position in the plane is denoted by $\mathbf{F}(\mathbf{s})$, and the reference and quadrature components of $\mathbf{F}$ at the point **s** are denoted by $[F_x(x, y), F_y(x, y)]$. By differentiating $\mathbf{F}(\mathbf{s})$ partially with respect to x and y, show that

$$\frac{\partial F_x}{\partial x} = \frac{\partial F_y}{\partial y}$$

$$\frac{\partial F_y}{\partial x} = -\frac{\partial F_x}{\partial y}$$

at points in the plane where $\mathbf{F}$ is an analytic function of **s** (Riemann-Cauchy equations).

5.25. Show that the Riemann-Cauchy equations in the previous problem may be written

$$\left(\frac{\partial}{\partial x}, \frac{\partial}{\partial y}\right) F_x = \left(\frac{\partial}{\partial y}, -\frac{\partial}{\partial x}\right) F_y .$$

Deduce that, at every point in the plane, there is equality in magnitude between the gradient of the reference component of **F** in any direction and the gradient of the quadrature component of **F** in the perpendicular direction. Deduce in particular that the direction of zero gradient for the reference component of **F** is perpendicular to the direction of zero gradient for the quadrature component of **F**.

5.26. If an analytic function $\mathbf{F}(\mathbf{s})$ is represented in the **s** plane by a contour map for the reference and quadrature components of **F**, deduce from the previous problem that the two sets of contours intersect each other at right angles. From Problem 5.23 deduce further that, if the function $\mathbf{F}(\mathbf{s})$ is represented in the **s** plane by a contour map for the magnitude and direction of **F**, then the angle contours intersect the magnitude contours at right angles. Hence show that the angle contours correspond to the lines of steepest ascent and descent on the terrain represented by the magnitude contours.

5.27. Deduce from the Riemann-Cauchy equations in Problem 5.24 that, if $\phi(x, y)$ is the reference component of any analytic vector function of the position vector in the (x, y) plane, then

$$\frac{\partial^2 \phi}{\partial x^2} + \frac{\partial^2 \phi}{\partial y^2} = 0.$$

Hence show that $\phi(x, y)$ satisfies the two-dimensional potential equation for (i) electrostatic fields, (ii) magnetostatic fields, and (iii) irrotational flow of incompressible fluids. Deduce that all of the contour maps encountered in this book may be interpreted as giving equipotential surfaces and lines of force, flux, or flow. Discuss some examples.

5.28. An analytic vector function **F** of a vector **s** is represented by a contour map in the **s** plane. A curve C is drawn in the plane from a point whose position vector is $\mathbf{s}_1$ to a point whose position vector is $\mathbf{s}_2$, and the curve is divided into elements of length. The vector element of length whose position vector is **s** is denoted by $d\mathbf{s}$ and it points along C from the point $\mathbf{s}_1$ to the point $\mathbf{s}_2$. For each element $d\mathbf{s}$ the planar product $\mathbf{F}(\mathbf{s})\, d\mathbf{s}$ is formed and these planar products are added vectorically for all the elements of length of C. It may be assumed that the vector sum tends to a limit as the lengths of the elements tend to zero and that this limit is written

$$\int_{\mathbf{s}_1}^{\mathbf{s}_2} \mathbf{F}(\mathbf{s})\, d\mathbf{s}$$

and is called the integral of $\mathbf{F}(\mathbf{s})$ along C from $\mathbf{s}_1$ to $\mathbf{s}_2$. Show that the integral of an analytic vector function of a vector between stated limits may be calculated by the same rules as the integral of an analytic scalar function of a scalar between stated limits.

5.29. Show that

$$\int_{\mathbf{s}_1}^{\mathbf{s}_2} e^{\mathbf{s}}\, d\mathbf{s} = e^{\mathbf{s}_2} - e^{\mathbf{s}_1}$$

and state the vector significance of this formula with the aid of the contour map for $e_{\mathbf{s}}$.

5.30. Show that

$$\int_{\mathbf{s}_1}^{\mathbf{s}_2} \cos \mathbf{s}\, d\mathbf{s} = \sin \mathbf{s}_2 - \sin \mathbf{s}_1$$

and state the vector significance of this formula with the aid of the contour maps for $\sin \mathbf{s}$ and $\cos \mathbf{s}$ derived in Problem 5.1.

INDEX